To Prof.

mit H

Be

ENDOCRINOLOGY

THE CHEMISTRY
OF THE
HORMONES

THE CHEMISTRY
OF THE
HORMONES

BY

BENJAMIN HARROW, Ph.D.

*Associate Professor of Chemistry, The City College,
College of the City of New York*

AND

CARL P. SHERWIN, D.Sc., M.D., Dr.P.H.

*On the staff of St. Vincent's Hospital and French Hospital,
New York City*

BALTIMORE
THE WILLIAMS & WILKINS COMPANY
1934

Composed and Printed at the
WAVERLY PRESS, INC.,
for
The Williams & Wilkins Company
Baltimore, Md., U. S. A.

PREFACE

As the title indicates, this book deals primarily with the *chemistry* of the hormones; though, of course, references to their physiological and clinical properties cannot well be excluded. The attempt has been made, in the following pages, to put together a *practical* book—a book of use to the laboratory worker who wishes to prepare active hormone fractions, or to isolate a chemically pure hormone; and of use to the student who wants a connected account dealing with the chemical characteristics of the hormones, in so far as they are known at present.

The references given at the end of each chapter represent articles which have proved useful in the preparation of this volume.

We are only too well aware that matters of importance may have been omitted, and that possibly some irrelevant matter may have been included. But that is the penalty which has to be paid when dealing with a subject in a state of flux.

For reading and criticizing individual chapters our best thanks are due to Professors J. B. Collip, McGill University; E. A. Doisy, St. Louis University; G. L. Foster, Columbia University; F. L. Hisaw, University of Wisconsin; A. C. Ivy, Northwestern University; H. Jensen, Johns Hopkins University; and W. W. Swingle, Princeton University. Dr. P. M. Apfelbaum has also offered several helpful suggestions.

April, 1934   BENJAMIN HARROW
                                                        CARL P. SHERWIN

CONTENTS

CHAPTER I

THE THYROID HORMONE

Since we are dealing with the chemistry of the hormones, a discussion of the thyroid gland is largely, though not entirely, a discussion of thyroxine, the hormone in the gland which has been both isolated and synthesized. To Kendall go the honors for first isolating the substance; but we owe to Harington (and to his collaborator, Barger) our knowledge of the chemical constitution of thyroxine, as well as a method for synthesizing the substance.

Without going into the history of the subject, which has been discussed by several authors (see, for example, (1) (21) (27)), we might mention two important observations prior to Kendall's contribution. One such observation was the discovery by Baumann, in 1895, that iodine is a normal constituent of the thyroid gland (2); the other, that all the iodine of the gland is bound up in a protein of the globulin class which may be extracted from the gland by a solution of salt. This protein, *iodothyroglobulin*, has a physiological activity similar to the entire gland (31). This second observation, made by Oswald in 1899, was the starting point for much subsequent work. Oswald extracted the glands with physiological salt solution and added an equal volume of saturated ammonium sulfate solution. The precipitate was dissolved in water and reprecipitated with ammonium sulfate. The material was next dialyzed until free from sulfate and then precipitated with 95 per cent alcohol, giving the iodothyroglobulin. A similar substance could also be obtained by dissolving the precipitate in alkali and precipitating with acetic acid. More recently, Harington (14) has isolated the substance by extracting the gland with 0.02 per cent sodium hydroxide and 1 per cent sodium chloride, allowing to stand

1

overnight and straining through muslin. The solid residue is again extracted. The combined extracts are chilled and the fat mechanically removed. The solution is now adjusted to pH 5.0, treated with sodium sulfate to make a 1 per cent concentration and raised to the boiling point. The coagulum, which contains 97 per cent of the total iodine in the extract is the crude iodothyroglobulin. Heidelberger and Palmer (14a) state that aqueous extracts of hog thyroids, when brought to a pH of 4.8 to 5.0, deposit nucleoprotein. After its removal, the thyroglobulin may be precipitated from the neutralized solution by one-half saturation with sodium sulfate or with ammonium sulfate.

ISOLATION OF THYROXINE

In 1915 (17) and more particularly in 1919 (18), Kendall published his method of isolating the active constituent, to which he gave the name *thyroxine* (contracted from thyroid oxindole). Earlier workers having failed to obtain active fractions by acid hydrolysis, Kendall tried alkaline hydrolysis. He found that thyroid material could be boiled with 5 per cent sodium hydroxide solution and the resulting product acidified, when a precipitate formed (the acid-insoluble part) which contained 40 per cent of the total iodine. The acid-soluble portion was practically inactive when tested physiologically; the acid-insoluble portion, however, could relieve symptoms of hypothyroidism when administered to patients. The method as finally published in 1919 was as follows (18): The fresh thyroid gland is hydrolyzed with 5 per cent sodium hydroxide. The fats are removed as insoluble salts. The clear, alkaline filtrate is cooled and acidified. The acid-insoluble constituent (containing thyroxine) is filtered off. The material is redissolved in sodium hydroxide and reprecipitated with hydrochloric acid. The precipitate is air-dried and treated with 95 per cent alcohol. The excess hydrochloric acid which remains in the air-dried precipitate is neutralized with sodium hydroxide until almost neutral to blue litmus. The heavy, black, tarry precipitate is removed by filtration. A hot, concentrated, aqueous solution of barium hydroxide is added to the alcoholic filtrate and the material refluxed. (Treatment with barium hydroxide removes heavy, dark impurities.) A small amount of sodium hydroxide is added to the filtrate and carbon dioxide is passed through the solution. The barium and sodium carbonates are removed by filtration and the alcohol is distilled. The aqueous residue is acidified with hydrochloric acid. The precipitate is dissolved in alkaline alcohol, carbon dioxide passed in, the precipitated sodium carbonate removed and the alcohol evaporated. The last traces of the alcohol are removed on the water-bath and the solution is allowed to stand. The mono-sodium salt of thyroxine (A) separates out. The yield is not quantitative. (A) may be further purified by dissolving in alkaline alcohol, passing in carbon dioxide and allowing the salt to crystallize a second time. The salt may then be dissolved in alkali (containing alcohol) and precipitated with acetic acid. This is repeated five times. The product is thyroxine. (See, also, (19) (20) (21) (22).)

In one of his more recent papers (21), Kendall discusses the advantages and the disadvantages of using sodium hydroxide or barium hydroxide for the hydrolysis of thyroid proteins. In this paper, published in 1928, Kendall gives a modified procedure for the isolation of thyroxine, which ought to be of value, since at this time he had had the opportunity of comparing his method with Harington's. Two kg. of sodium hydroxide are dissolved in 5 liters of water, 22.5 kg. of fresh thyroid glands are added, and the total volume is made up to 30 liters. The solution is heated for 24 hours at 95° to 100°, then poured into 20 liters of water containing 8 kg. of salt, and the layer of fat is mechanically removed. A few kg. of ice are next added and the solution is made acid with hydrochloric acid. The precipitate is dissolved in 10 liters of 5 per cent sodium hydroxide and the solution is heated for 18 hours. Four hundred to 500 grams of crystalline barium hydroxide, dissolved in hot water, are added to the solution, which is now heated for an additional 3 hours. (The barium hydroxide precipitates all of the fatty acids which are present and also carries out of solution a large amount of black, tarry impurities. Thyroxine is not precipitated at this point.)

The precipitate is filtered and the filtrate is acidified with hydrochloric acid. A small flocculent precipitate (Fraction A) separates. (A) is dissolved in a total volume of 500 cc. of water containing from 200 to 250 grams of crystalline barium hydroxide. Ammonia is added to assist solution. The material is heated for 18 to 20 hours, the solution is filtered hot and the barium-insoluble material is decomposed with sodium hydroxide and sodium sulfate (B). (B) is acidified, and the heavy, black, tarry precipitate is dried and weighed. One part of this material is dissolved in 150 parts of 95 per cent alcohol containing a small amount of hydrochloric acid. The solution is cooled to 10° and powdered sodium hydroxide is added until red litmus paper turns faintly blue. The sodium salt of the black, tarry impurities is almost entirely insoluble and can be removed by filtration. The separation of the impurities is made more complete by the addition of 3 to 4 grams of sodium hydroxide and treatment of the solution with carbon dioxide. The sodium carbonate and precipitated material are filtered out, the light colored filtrate is acidified with acetic acid and slowly evaporated, when thyroxine, in the form of a white, crystalline precipitate separates out.

Kendall, on the basis of somewhat slender evidence, had suggested an indole formula for thyroxine. "The stability of the compound," writes Harington in his first paper (7), "particularly towards boiling alkali, is scarcely consistent

with the supposed existence in the molecule of a 2,4,6-tri-
hydro-2,4,6-triiodoindole nucleus.   The supposition that the
compound is an indole derivative is apparently based on the
fact that, under certain conditions, it gives the pine-splinter
reaction; but here again the other properties of the substance,
its relative stability towards oxidising agents and, when pure,
towards acids, are not such as would be expected from a
consideration of the known properties of indole derivatives
of a somewhat similar constitution to that proposed for
thyroxine." Harington, however, first synthesized 3,4,5-
triiodophenylpyrrolidone carboxylic acid, a substance having
practically the same formula as that of thyroxine proposed
by Kendall; it was totally devoid of activity as tested by the
basal metabolic rate.

Harington next turned his attention to ways by which the
yield of thyroxine could be improved.[1]   Kendall had obtained something like 33 grams of thyroxine from 3 tons of
thyroid gland.   This made an investigation of the chemical
properties of the hormone far from easy.   Harington (8)
found that an initial hydrolysis with barium hydroxide
rather than with sodium hydroxide had advantages.   The
filtrate contained 60 to 70 per cent of the total iodine, of which
40 per cent could be precipitated with acid.   Harington
could find no way at this stage of causing a separation of
thyroxine.   He therefore treated the product with more
barium hydroxide.   This led to a further separation of iodine,
50 per cent remaining in solution and the remainder being
carried down with the insoluble salts.   The portion which
remained in solution could not be precipitated with acid.
The barium salts were boiled with alkali and sodium sulfate
and the product reprecipitated with acids.   The precipitate
was dissolved in alkaline alcohol and precipitated with acetic acid.   This yielded a partially crystalline product containing 63 per cent of iodine.   Fourteen per cent of the total

[1] While this chapter was being written, Harington's book (11a) appeared.

iodine of the gland was obtained as thyroxine. The yield
(calculated on the basis of fresh gland) was 0.027 per cent,
as compared to 0.0011 per cent obtained by Kendall. An
analysis gave the formula $C_{15}H_{11}O_4NI_4$, rather than Kendall's $C_{11}H_{10}O_3NI_3$.

To isolate thyroxine, Harington boils 500 grams of desiccated thyroid gland with 5 liters of 10 per cent crystalline
barium hydroxide under reflux. The product is allowed to
stand overnight and then filtered. A heavy dark precipitate
(B) remains. The filtrate is acidified to Congo red with
acetic acid, the precipitate (A) is allowed to settle, filtered
and washed with water. The filtrate from (A) is rejected.
(A) is dissolved in 250 cc. of water, with the aid of ammonia,
treated with crystalline barium hydroxide to make a concentration of 40 per cent of the latter, boiled to drive off the
excess of ammonia and heated for 18 hours on a steam bath
under reflux. The product is filtered hot and the precipitate
(C) is washed with a little hot water. The filtrate from (C)
is discarded. (C) is ground, suspended in 250 cc. of 1 per
cent sodium hydroxide, boiled, and, while boiling, treated
with a strong solution of sodium sulfate in slight excess. The
material is filtered from the barium sulfate, the filtrate is
heated to boiling and, while boiling, is treated with 50 per
cent sulfuric acid until acid to Congo red. The precipitate
is filtered, dissolved in 20 cc. of N sodium hydroxide, and
alcohol is added to 80 per cent concentration. The material is filtered from a small amount of tar, brought to the
boiling point and treated with 10 cc. of 33 per cent acetic
acid. Thyroxine separates out in partially crystalline form.

The precipitate from the preliminary hydrolysis (B) is
boiled with 500 cc. of 2 per cent sodium hydroxide, together with a slight excess of sodium sulfate, filtered, the
filtrate acidified with hydrochloric acid, and the precipitate
treated similarly to (A). This produces a further yield of
thyroxine.

The crude thyroxine can be purified by dissolving in alkali and precipitating with acetic acid. But an even better method is to make use of the insolubility of its sodium salt. After one recrystallization, the crude material is dissolved in boiling 0.5 per cent sodium carbonate (75 cc. per 1 gram) and cooled, when the sodium salt of thyroxine, in the form of a white precipitate, separates out. This is allowed to stand in the ice-chest overnight, centrifuged, dissolved in 80 to 90 per cent of alcohol containing a little sodium hydroxide, brought to boiling and treated with 33 per cent of acetic acid in excess. The white crystalline product so produced is purified thyroxine. It darkens at 220° and melts with decomposition at 231° to 233°.

Pure thyroxine is insoluble in water and all ordinary organic solvents. It is soluble in the cold in solutions of alkalies, provided that the concentration of alkali is not too high. It can be precipitated from alkaline solutions by means of acid. The hormone dissolves in a solution of sodium carbonate only on boiling. It is soluble in 90 per cent alcohol provided an alkaline hydroxide or a mineral acid (but not acetic) is present. (See, also, (30).)

Harington records that 10 mg. of his preparation was given intravenously to a normal individual with a basal metabolism of −5. On the fifth day the basal metabolic rate reached +40, and the pulse had increased from 72 to 120.

Very recently, Foster (23), in devising a method for the determination of thyroxine in the thyroid gland (which is based upon the fact that thyroxine can be separated from other iodine compounds present after alkaline hydrolysis by extraction with butyl alcohol), has also suggested a method for isolating the hormone.

Blau (2a) has suggested a method of estimating thyroxine which is based upon the insolubility of the hormone in acid solution and upon the solubility of the acid salt of the product in butyl alcohol.

CONSTITUTION OF THYROXINE

In the very next paper, and in the same year (1926), Harington records the constitution and synthesis of *desiodo-thyroxine*, that is thyroxine without its iodine atoms (9). It was soon clear to him that unless the iodine atoms were first removed from the thyroid molecule, the chances of getting at the constitution of the latter were slim. This was done by shaking a 1 per cent thyroxine solution in N potassium hydroxide with hydrogen, in the presence of the catalyst palladium hydroxide-calcium carbonate. The iodine was split off quantitatively as potassium iodide and an almost theoretical yield of iodine-free thyroxine (desiodo-thyroxine) (A) was obtained. The hydrogen taken up was equivalent to the iodine split off (4 atoms per molecule of thyroxine). (A) upon analysis gave the formula $C_{15}H_{15}O_4N$. It gave the Millon and the ninhydrin reactions and yielded all the nitrogen with nitrous acid in the Van Slyke apparatus. It formed salts with acid and alkali. This led to the view that it was probably an alpha-amino acid with at least one phenolic grouping. The proportion of carbon to hydrogen suggested the presence of two benzene rings. Fusion with potassium hydroxide gave a large percentage of a compound with the formula $C_{13}H_{12}O_2$. This compound yielded a mono-benzoyl derivative, suggesting at this stage that one oxygen atom was part of a phenolic grouping, whereas the second oxygen atom was inert.

This preliminary exploration yielded sufficient information so that an attempted synthesis of desiodo-thyroxine could now be undertaken.

p-Bromoanisole was condensed with the potassium salt of *p*-cresol, in the presence of copper bronze, to give 4-(4 methoxyphenoxy) toluene (I):

(I) boiled with hydrogen iodide gave 4-(4'-hydroxyphenoxy) toluene (II)

$$HO\langle\ \rangle-O-\langle\ \rangle CH_3 \qquad\qquad II$$

which proved identical with the compound $C_{13}H_{12}O_2$ which was obtained when desiodo-thyroxine was fused.

Boiled with potassium permanganate, (I) was converted into the corresponding acid: 4-(4'-methoxyphenoxy) benzoic acid (III):

$$CH_3O\langle\ \rangle-O-\langle\ \rangle COOH \qquad\qquad III$$

which proved to be identical with an acid, $C_{14}H_{12}O_4$, obtained as the final oxidation product of desiodo-thyroxine after methylation.

Using strictly analogous methods, p-bromoanisole was now condensed with potassium phenolate, giving 4-(4'-methoxyphenoxy) benzene (IV):

$$CH_3O\langle\ \rangle Br + HO\langle\ \rangle \xrightarrow[Cu]{KOH}$$

$$CH_3O\langle\ \rangle-O-\langle\ \rangle \qquad\qquad IV$$

from this, by Gattermann's HCN method, 4-(4'-methoxyphenoxy) benzaldehyde (V) was prepared

$$CH_3O\langle\ \rangle-O-\langle\ \rangle CHO \qquad\qquad V$$

the constitution of which was confirmed by the fact that (V) on oxidation yielded (III).

From this aldehyde it was then possible to synthesize 4-(4'-methoxyphenoxy) cinnamic acid (VI)

$$CH_3O\langle\ \rangle-O-\langle\ \rangle CH:CH\cdot COOH \qquad\qquad VI$$

and finally desiodo-thyroxine itself.

This desiodo-thyroxine was synthesized by two methods: (a) glycine anhydride was condensed with (V) in the presence of acetic anhydride and sodium acetate. On boiling the product with hydrogen iodide and red phosphorus, it underwent simultaneous reduction, hydrolysis and demethylation, with the formation of β-(4-(4'-hydroxyphenoxy) phenyl)-α-aminopropionic acid (VII):

$$2 \text{ of } V + CH_2 \left\langle \begin{matrix} NH-CO \\ CO-NH \end{matrix} \right\rangle CH_2 \xrightarrow[+\bar{A}_2O]{Na\bar{A}}$$

$$CH_3O\langle\rangle-O-\langle\rangle CH$$
$$\ddot{C}$$
$$HN \qquad CO$$
$$O\dot{C} \qquad NH$$
$$C$$
$$CH_3O\langle\rangle-O-\langle\rangle \ddot{C}H$$
$$P \mid HI$$
$$2 \text{ HO}\langle\rangle-O-\langle\rangle CH_2 \cdot CH \cdot COOH$$
$$NH_2 \qquad\qquad VII$$

(b) or another method to prepare (VII) is to condense (V) with hydantoin and boil the product with hydrogen iodide and red phosphorus:

$$V + H_2C \text{———} CO \xrightarrow[\bar{A}_2O]{Na\bar{A}}$$
$$HN \qquad NH$$
$$CO$$

$$CH_3O\langle\rangle-O-\langle\rangle CH:C \text{———} CO \xrightarrow[P]{HI} \quad VII$$
$$HN \qquad NH$$
$$CO$$

By both methods, (a) and (b), a product was obtained which was in every way identical with the desiodothyroxine obtained from thyroxine itself.

(VII) is obviously the *p*-hydroxy phenyl ether of tyrosine; and it was clear that not tryptophane but tyrosine must be looked upon as the mother substance of thyroxine.

The following year (1927) Harington, together with Barger, published their now celebrated paper on the synthesis of thyroxine (12). Incidentally, a footnote on the first page reveals that Dakin in this country was about to publish a paper on thyroxine, in which, among other things, he showed that fusing thyroxine with fuming hydrogen iodide at 140° converts it into tyrosine.

That thyroxine is a tetraiodo derivative of the *p*-hydroxy-phenyl ether of tyrosine was clear from Harington's previous work. The exact positions of the iodine atoms had now to be determined. And, of course, the synthesis of thyroxine itself had to be undertaken.

With regard to the position of the iodine atoms, the supposition was made that thyroxine is formed in nature by coupling together two molecules of 3:5-diiodotyrosine.

Quinol monomethyl ether was condensed with 3:4:5-tri-iodonitrobenzene to give 3:5-diiodo-4-(4'-methoxyphenoxy) nitrobenzene (I)

$$\text{CH}_3\text{O} \langle \ \rangle \text{OH} + \text{I} \langle \ \rangle \text{NO}_2 \rightarrow \text{CH}_3\text{O} \langle \ \rangle \text{--O--} \langle \ \rangle \text{NO}_2;$$

I

this compound was reduced to the corresponding aniline (II)

$$\text{CH}_3\text{O} \langle \ \rangle \text{--O--} \langle \ \rangle \text{NH}_2 \qquad \text{II}$$

and the latter converted, by means of the Sandmeyer reaction, into the nitrile (III)

$$CH_3O\langle\ \rangle\!-\!O\!-\!\overset{\displaystyle I}{\underset{\displaystyle I}{\langle\ \rangle}}\!CN \qquad\qquad III$$

This nitrile, on boiling with a mixture of hydrogen iodide and acetic acid, underwent simultaneous hydrolysis and demethylation, yielding 3:5-diiodo-4-(4′-hydroxyphenoxy)benzoic acid (IV)

$$HO\langle\ \rangle\!-\!O\!-\!\overset{\displaystyle I}{\underset{\displaystyle I}{\langle\ \rangle}}\!COOH \qquad\qquad IV$$

On the addition of iodine in potassium iodide to a solution of this acid in concentrated ammonia, iodine was rapidly taken up until two molecules had been absorbed, and there was obtained 3:5-diiodo-4-(3′:5′-diiodo-4′-hydroxyphenoxy) benzoic acid (V)

$$HO\overset{\displaystyle I}{\underset{\displaystyle I}{\langle\ \rangle}}\!-\!O\overset{\displaystyle I}{\underset{\displaystyle I}{\langle\ \rangle}}\!COOH; \qquad\qquad V$$

on methylation this gave an acid (VI)

$$CH_3O\overset{\displaystyle I}{\underset{\displaystyle I}{\langle\ \rangle}}\!-\!O\!-\!\overset{\displaystyle I}{\underset{\displaystyle I}{\langle\ \rangle}}\!COOH \qquad\qquad VI$$

which proved to be identical with the acid obtained by methylation and subsequent oxidation of thyroxine. "This series of experiments, therefore, settled beyond doubt the question of the orientation of the iodine atoms in thyroxine, since it is certain that the last two iodine atoms, introduced into the acid (IV) in alkaline solution, must have entered the *ortho* position to the free phenolic group."

For the actual synthesis of thyroxine, Harington and Barger started with 3:5-diiodo-4-(4′-methoxyphenoxy) benzaldehyde (VII)

$$CH_3O\langle\ \rangle-O-\langle\ \rangle CHO, \qquad \text{VII}$$

which was obtained from the nitrile (III) by the use of anhydrous stannous chloride. After many trials, VII was condensed with hippuric acid, in the presence of sodium acetate to give the azlactone (VIII)

$$CH_3O\langle\ \rangle-O-\langle\ \rangle CH : C \underset{\displaystyle N}{\overset{\displaystyle |}{\ }} \begin{matrix} CO \\ | \\ O, \end{matrix} \qquad \text{VIII}$$

$$\overset{\displaystyle N}{\underset{\displaystyle C \cdot C_6H_5}{\|}}$$

which, when warmed with alcohol and sulfuric acid, was converted into the corresponding α-benzoylaminocinnamic ester (IX)

$$CH_3O\langle\ \rangle-O-\langle\ \rangle CH : C(NH \cdot CO \cdot C_6H_5)COOEt; \quad \text{IX}$$

and this, on boiling with hydrogen iodide and red phosphorus, gave β-(3:5-diiodo-4-(4′-hydroxyphenoxy))phenyl-α-aminopropionic acid (X).

$$HO\langle\ \rangle-O-\langle\ \rangle CH_2 \cdot \underset{\displaystyle NH_2}{\overset{\displaystyle |}{CH}} \cdot COOH \qquad \text{X}$$

(X) was dissolved in concentrated ammonia and treated, drop by drop, with N iodine in potassium iodide, yielding β-(3:5-diiodo-4(3′:5′-diiodo-4′-hydroxyphenoxy))phenyl-α-aminopropionic acid, or thyroxine (XI)

$$HO\langle\ \rangle\!\!-\!\!O\!\!-\!\!\langle\ \rangle CH_2 \cdot CH \cdot COOH. \qquad XI$$
$$\underset{NH_2}{|}$$

The melting point of the synthetic thyroxine proved to be 231° (with decomposition). When mixed with a sample of natural thyroxine, with a melting point of 228°, it melted at 228°. It gave with intensity a color reaction with nitrous acid and ammonia which is given by thyroxine. The solubilities of the natural and synthetic products, including their sodium salts, were entirely similar. Dr. Lyon used the synthetic thyroxine in two myxedema cases, and the rise in basal metabolism was similar to that obtained when the natural product was used (24).

RESOLUTION OF *dl*-THYROXINE

Alkaline hydrolysis of the thyroid gland yields the racemic compound. To get the optically active forms of thyroxine,[2] Harington (10) decided to resolve first *dl*-3:5-diiodothyronine (I) into optically active compounds and then iodinate them. This became necessary because of the extreme insolubility of thyroxine itself, which made the preparation and purification of its salts a matter of difficulty. (I) with anhydrous formic acid yielded the formyl derivative (II), soluble in alcohol and insoluble in water. However, the alkaloid salts

---

[2] In this paper Harington suggests a simpler nomenclature. He proposes that desiodothyroxine be called *thyronine*, the positions being numbered thus:

$$HO\ \underset{3'\ 2'}{\overset{5'\ 6'}{\langle\ \rangle}}\!\!-\!\!0\!\!-\!\!\underset{3\ 2}{\overset{5\ 6}{\langle\ \rangle}}CH_2\cdot CH\cdot COOH$$
$$\underset{NH_2}{|}$$

which means that thyroxine becomes 3:5:3′:5′-tetraiodothyronine.

of (II) would not crystallize.   Success crowned his efforts by
the use of the two isomerides of α-phenylethylamine.   The
formyl derivative was first prepared by warming (I) with 99
per cent formic acid.   The excess formic acid was distilled
off and the residue was extracted with absolute alcohol,
filtered, the filtrate boiled with charcoal, filtered and poured
into an excess of hot water.   Formyl-3,5-diiodothyronine
(II) crystallized out.   (II) was next combined with l-phenyl-
ethylamine, the acid was recovered from this salt combination,
the HCO group was removed by hydrolysis with hydrogen bromide, and the resulting optically active diiodothyro-
nine iodinated.   In this way, the l-α-phenylethylamine gave
l-thyroxine, $[(\alpha)]_{5461}^{21°} -3.2°$; and the d-α-phenylethylamine
gave d-thyroxine, $[(\alpha)]_{5461}^{21} +2.97°$. The l-modification proved
three times more active than the $d-$.

In a subsequent paper (14) Harington records the isolation
of a small quantity of l-thyroxine by the action of proteolytic
enzymes on the gland.

DERIVATIVES OF THYROXINE

The best effects with thyroxine are obtained when it is
administered intravenously.   Harington is of the opinion
that the pure hormone is poorly absorbed after oral administration because of its extreme insolubility.   He believes that
the mere fact that drastic hydrolysis is necessary in order to
isolate thyroxine points to the presence of thyroxine in the
gland as a constituent of a peptid or protein molecule; which,
if true, would probably make the substance more soluble and
would explain why the crude thyroid gland as a therapeutic
agent is so effective when administered orally.   With this
in view, Harington (11) prepared the glycyl- and the dl-
alanylthyroxine, without, however, finding them more
soluble than the mother substance.   He also prepared thy-
roxamine, by the decarboxylation of thyroxine and showed
that when used with tadpoles it behaved similarly to thyroxine, but, strangely enough, it showed no pressor effect.

Myers (29) has prepared the O-methyl- and the O-methyl-N-acetyl-,*dl*-thyroxine. Substitution of the hydroxyl group diminishes the effect of thyroxine on amphibian metamorphosis. O-methylthyroxine, in amounts comparable with the physiological dose of thyroxine, produces no effect when administered intravenously to a normal individual.

3,5-DIIODOTYROSINE

Physiologically inactive though this compound is,[3] it nevertheless is of interest because its structure suggests that it may be a precursor of thyroxine itself. At about the same time, though quite independently, Foster (3) in this country and Harington (13) in England isolated the compound from the thyroid gland. Both processes also include the preparation of thyroxine; but of the two, the method developed by Foster seems the simpler and the more economical.

Foster's method of isolation is based on the slight solubility of the lead salt of diiodotyrosine and the use of phosphotungstic acid to remove interfering substances. One hundred grams of partially purified thyroglobulin, 400 grams of crystallized barium hydroxide and 1000 cc. of water were boiled under a reflux for 18 hours and filtered hot. The filtrate was chilled and the barium hydroxide crystals filtered off and washed with cold water. The filtrate was strongly acidified with glacial acetic acid (50 cc. beyond the maximum red color of methyl red), and the precipitate which formed was allowed to remain in the ice-box for two days. Thyroxine was prepared from this precipitate by crystallizing the sodium salt from dilute sodium carbonate, then precipitating from alkaline alcohol with acetic acid, as already described (p. 6).

To the filtrate were added 100 grams of lead acetate in a

---

[3] This is not strictly true, for together with thyroxine it accelerates metamorphosis in amphibia, but it has no effect on the basal metabolic rate in normal individuals (6).

small amount of water and the solution was filtered from lead sulfide. Ammonia was added to the filtrate till alkaline to phenolphthalein. The precipitate was collected and washed by grinding with 0.1 per cent ammonia. It was suspended in water, acidified with glacial acetic acid, the insoluble material removed by filtration and dilute sulfuric acid added till acid to congo red. The lead sulfate was filtered off. To the filtrate were added 10 grams of phosphotungstic acid in concentrated solution and the precipitate removed by filtration. Phosphotungstic and sulfuric acids were removed by barium hydroxide in slight excess. The solution was next acidified with acetic acid, 50 grams of lead acetate added, and the lead salt precipitated by the addition of ammonia, as before. The precipitate was collected, washed with water and decomposed with hydrogen sulfide. The filtrate from the lead sulfide was evaporated under reduced pressure to about 15 cc. and placed in the cold. The crystals were dissolved in a few drops of water and reprecipitated with acetic acid. The crystals contained 58.3 per cent of iodine, melted at 197° when heated slowly and at 203° when heated rapidly. From a sample of 100 grams of thyroglobulin, 33 per cent of the total iodine was isolated as diiodotyrosine and 16 per cent as thyroxine; leaving much iodine still to be accounted for.

Harington's method (13), which also includes the isolation of thyroxine as well as diiodotyrosine, is more involved. Two hundred and fifty grams of desiccated thyroid gland are boiled under reflux for 6 hours with 2500 cc. of 10 per cent barium hydroxide. After cooling, the solution is filtered (A). The filtrate (B) is brought up to pH 5.0 with 50 per cent sulfuric acid. The precipitate of thyroxine and barium sulfate, which also carries down some of the acid-soluble iodine by adsorption, is filtered off (C) and the filtrate and the washings (D) are set aside.

For the isolation of thyroxine, the insoluble barium salts

which are left undissolved after the initial hydrolysis (A) are ground up, suspended in dilute hydrochloric acid, the solution is heated to boiling, adjusted to pH 5.0 and filtered. The precipitate is ground up with ether, again filtered and dissolved in sodium hydroxide. The resulting solution is combined with (C) after the latter has been extracted with warm dilute sodium hydroxide and the barium sulfate had been removed. The sodium hydroxide solutions are acidified with sulfuric acid to pH 5.0, the precipitate filtered off (F), the solution treated with a slight excess of barium hydroxide and the filtrate (E) reserved. The acid-insoluble precipitate (F) is dissolved in 300 cc. of water with the aid of a little ammonia, crystalline barium hydroxide is added to 40 per cent concentration and the whole heated for 18 hours at 100°. The solution is filtered hot (G), the filtrate (H) cooled, and the barium hydroxide which separates is removed. Hydrochloric acid is next added to pH 5.0 and the precipitate (I) collected.

The insoluble barium salts (G) are decomposed by boiling with sodium hydroxide and sodium sulfate, and to the alkaline filtrate is added (I). The alkaline solution is heated to boiling and brought to pH 5.0 with sulfuric acid. The precipitate is collected and dissolved in 80 per cent alcohol, with the aid of sodium hydroxide. The solution is filtered, heated to boiling, acidified with acetic acid, and thyroxine separates.

For the isolation of diiodotyrosine, the filtrate (D) is treated with basic lead acetate until no further precipitate forms. The lead salts are filtered off and suspended in two liters of water. The mixture is heated to boiling and 50 per cent sulfuric acid is added until acid to congo red. The lead sulfate is removed by filtration, and the filtrate is freed from sulfuric acid by the addition of a slight excess of barium hydroxide. The alkaline filtrate from the barium sulfate is combined with (E), and the whole is boiled down to 500 cc. Two hundred grams of crystallized barium hydroxide are added and the solution is heated for 18 hours at 100°. The precipitate is filtered, the filtrate cooled and the barium hydroxide filtered off and recrystallized. The combined mother liquors are treated with carbon dioxide, and the barium carbonate is removed by filtration and washed. Silver nitrate is now added to the filtrate until precipitation is complete. The silver salts are filtered off, ground up with dilute nitric acid and filtered. The organic silver salts (which dissolve) are reprecipitated with ammonia, filtered, washed, suspended in water and decomposed with hydrogen sulfide. The solution is heated to boiling, the silver sulfide is removed by filtration, and the filtrate is concentrated to 200 cc. *in vacuo.*

The solution is extracted with butyl alcohol at 70°, the butyl alcoholic extract is evaporated to dryness under diminished pressure, and the residue is dissolved in water up to 500 cc. The solution is boiled and uranium acetate, in slight excess, is added. The precipitate is filtered, the filtrate is freed from uranium with ammonia and concentrated to 320 cc. *in vacuo.* Basic lead acetate is now added and the precipitate which forms is allowed to stand overnight. The precipitate is decomposed with hydrogen sulfide, the filtrate is concentrated, the solution is neutralized and finally concentrated in a vacuum desiccator. The crystalline compound which deposits is recrystallized from 50 per cent acetic acid.

The melting point of the diiodotyrosine Harington found to be 198.4° (with decomposition). The analysis showed the following:

	I	N
Found	58.2	2.8, 2.9
Calculated for $C_9H_9O_3NI_2$	58.6	3.2

A schematic outline of this preparation is shown on page 20.

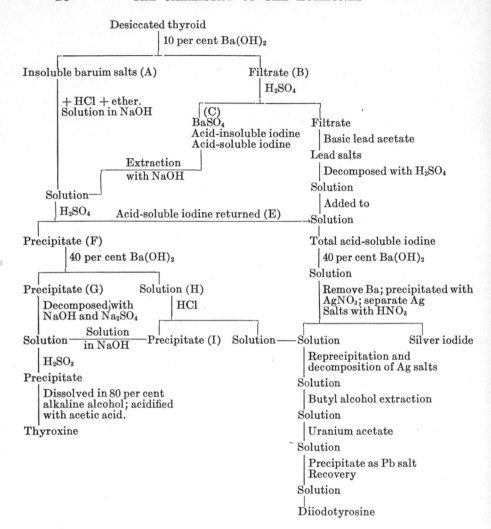

Desiccated thyroid
| 10 per cent $Ba(OH)_2$

Insoluble baruim salts (A)   Filtrate (B)
| H_2SO_4

+ HCl + ether.
Solution in NaOH
                    (C)
                    $BaSO_4$
                    Acid-insoluble iodine   Filtrate
                    Acid-soluble iodine | Basic lead acetate
                                                   Lead salts
            Extraction | Decomposed with H_2SO_4
            with NaOH   Solution
    Solution | Added to
    | H_2SO_4 Acid-soluble iodine returned (E) →Solution

Precipitate (F)   Total acid-soluble iodine
    | 40 per cent $Ba(OH)_2$ | 40 per cent $Ba(OH)_2$
                                                  Solution
Precipitate (G)   Solution (H)   Remove Ba; precipitated with
    Decomposed with | HCl $AgNO_3$; separate Ag
    NaOH and Na_2SO_4 Salts with HNO_3
            Solution
Solution   in NaOH   Precipitate (I) Solution—Solution   Silver iodide
    | H_2SO_3 Reprecipitation and
Precipitate   decomposition of Ag salts
    Dissolved in 80 per cent   Solution
    alkaline alcohol; acidified | Butyl alcohol extraction
    with acetic acid.   Solution
Thyroxine | Uranium acetate
                                                  Solution
                                                  Precipitate as Pb salt
                                                  Recovery
                                                  Solution
                                                  | Diiodotyrosine

PHYSIOLOGICAL TESTS FOR THYROID (AND THYROXINE) ACTIVITY

The details of these tests, together with their application to methods for standardizing thyroid material are discussed by Kendall (21) and Munch (28), among others. One such

test we owe to a discovery by Gudernatsch (5) who showed
that the metamorphosis of tadpoles was hastened by feeding
them thyroid gland (or thyroxine, as has since been discovered). The shortening of the tail during metamorphosis
has been used for delicate quantitative studies of thyroxine
(4). Another, and a more important quantitative study, is
the effect of the thyroid (or thyroxine) upon basal metabolism. In a patient with high-grade myxedema, 1 mg. of
thyroxine produces an increase of 2.8 per cent of the normal
value. From 6 to 8 days are required before thyroxine
exerts its maximum effect; and the basal metabolism does not
return to normal until 4 to 5 weeks later. Still a third test
we owe to Reid Hunt, who showed that thyroid material
(and thyroxine) increases the resistance of mice (and mice
only) to the action of acetonitrile (15, 16).

Curtis and co-workers (2b) find the iodine content of the
blood to be a measure of thyroid function. The blood iodine
is increased in hyperfunction and lowered in hypofunction.
Corresponding changes occur in urinary excretion of iodine.

GOITER AND IODINE

This subject, the relation of iodine to endemic goiter, is
discussed by Marine (25), McClendon (27) and Levine and
Remington (23a), among others.

PHYSIOLOGICAL AND CLINICAL APPLICATIONS

See the splendid article by Marine (26).[4] (See also, (2a).)

REFERENCES

(1) BARGER, G.: Some applications of organic chemistry to biology and
medicine. (McGraw-Hill Co., New York. 1930.)
(1a) BARNES, B. O.: Preparation of thyroglobulin. *Proc. Soc. Exp. Biol.
and Med.*, **29**, 680 (1932).
(2) BAUMANN, E.: Ueber das normale Vorkommen von Jod im Tierkörper.
Zt. physiol. Chem., **21**, 319 (1895–1896).

[4] It must be recalled here that the anterior pituitary contains a thyroid-
stimulating hormone (See p. 88).

(2a) BLAU, N. F.: The determination of thyroxine in the thyroid gland. *J. Biol. Chem.*, **102**, 269 (1933).

(2b) CURTIS, G. M., DAVIS, C. B. AND PHILLIPS, F. J.: Significance of the iodine content of human blood. *J. Am. Med. Assoc.*, **101**, 901 (1933).

(3) FOSTER, G. L.: The isolation of 3,5-diiodo-tyrosine from the thyroid. *J. Biol. Chem.*, **83**, 345 (1929).

(4) GADDUM, J. H.: Quantitative observations on thyroxine and allied substances. I. The use of tadpoles. *J. Physiol.*, **64**, 246 (1927).

(5) GUDERNATSCH, J. F.: Studies on internal secretion. IV. Treatment of tadpoles with thyroid and thymus extracts. *Anat. Record*, **11**, 357 (1917).

(6) GUTMAN, A. B., SLOAN, L. W., GUTMAN, E. B. AND PALMER, W. W.: The rôle of diiodotyrosine in hyperthyroidism. *J. Am. Med. Assoc.*, **101**, 256 (1933).

(7) HARINGTON, C. R.: Synthesis of 3,4,5-triiodophenylpyrrolidone carboxylic acid, a possible isomer of thyroxine. *J. Biol. Chem.*, **64**, 23 (1925).

(8) HARINGTON, C. R.: Chemistry of thyroxine. Isolation of thyroxine from the thyroid gland. *Biochem. J.*, **20**, 293 (1926).

(9) HARINGTON, C. R.: Constitution and synthesis of desiodo-thyroxine. *Biochem. J.*, **20**, 300 (1926).

(10) HARINGTON, C. R.: Resolution of *dl*-thyroxine. *Biochem. J.*, **22**, 1429 (1928).

(11) HARINGTON, C. R.: Some derivatives of thyroxine. *Biochem. J.*, **22**, 1436 (1928).

(11a) HARINGTON, C. R.: The thyroid gland. (Oxford Univ. Press, London. 1933).

(12) HARINGTON, C. R. AND BARGER, G.: Chemistry of thyroxine; constitution and synthesis of thyroxine. *Biochem. J.*, **21**, 169 (1927).

(13) HARINGTON, C. R. AND RANDALL, S. S.: Observations on the iodine-containing compounds of the thyroid gland. Isolation of *dl*-3:5-diiodotyrosine. *Biochem. J.*, **23**, 373 (1929).

(14) HARINGTON, C. R. AND SALTER, W. T.: Isolation of *l*-thyroxine from the thyroid gland by the action of proteolytic enzymes. *Biochem. J.*, **24**, 456 (1930).

(14a) HEIDELBERGER, M. AND PALMER, W. W.: The preparation and properties of thyroglobulin. *J. Biol. Chem.*, **101**, 433 (1933).

(15) HUNT, R.: The influence of thyroid feeding upon poisoning by acetonitrile. *J. Biol. Chem.*, **1**, 33 (1905).

(16) HUNT, R.: The acetonitril test for thyroid and of some alterations of metabolism. *Am. J. Physiol.*, **63**, 257 (1923).

(17) KENDALL, E. C.: A method for the decomposition of the proteins of the thyroid, with a description of certain constituents. *J. Biol. Chem.*, **20**, 501 (1915).

(18) KENDALL, E. C.: Isolation of the iodine compound which occurs in the thyroid. *J. Biol. Chem.*, **39**, 125 (1919).

(19) KENDALL, E. C.: Chemistry of the thyroid secretion. *Harvey Society Lectures.* (Lippincott, Philadelphia. 1920–1921).

(20) KENDALL, E. C.: Isolation of thyroxin. *J. Biol. Chem.*, **72**, 213 (1927).

(21) KENDALL, E. C.: Thyroxine (Chem. Catalog Co., New York. 1929).

(22) KENDALL, E. C. AND SIMONSEN, D. G.: Seasonal variations in the iodine and thyroxine content of the thyroid gland. *J. Biol. Chem.*, **80**, 357 (1928).

(23) LELAND, J. P. AND FOSTER, G. L.: A method for the determination of thyroxine in the thyroid. *J. Biol. Chem.*, **95**, 165 (1932).

(23a) LEVINE, H. AND REMINGTON, R. E.: Is goiter due to an iodine deficiency per se? *J. Chem. Educ.*, **10**, 649 (1933).

(24) LYON, D. M.: Note on physiological test of synthetic thyroxine. *Biochem. J.*, **21**, 181 (1927).

(25) MARINE, D.: Etiology and prevention of simple goiter. *Harvey Lectures.* (Lippincott, Philadelphia. 1923–1924), p. 96.

(26) MARINE, D.: The present status of the functions of the thyroid gland. *Physiol. Rev.*, **2**, 521 (1922).

(27) McCLENDON, J. F.: The distribution of iodine with special reference to goiter. *Physiol. Rev.*, **7**, 189 (1927).

(28) MUNCH, J. C.: Biossays (Williams & Wilkins, Baltimore. 1931).

(29) MYERS, C. S.: Some derivatives of diiodotyrosine and thyroxine. *J. Am. Chem. Soc.*, **54**, 3718 (1932).

(30) New and Non-official Remedies, 1933 (American Med. Assoc. Chicago).

(31) OSWALD, A.: Die Eiweisskörper der Schilddrüse. *Zt. physiol. Chem.*, **27**, 14 (1899).

(32) OSWALD, A.: Zur Kenntniss des Thyreoglobulins. *Zt. physiol. Chem.*, **32**, 121 (1901).

Chapter II

THE PARATHYROID HORMONE

The history of the parathyroid hormone centers itself very largely around the pioneer work of Collip. Since the discovery by Gley in 1891 of the external pair of parathyroid glands, the tetany and ultimate death which results from their removal have been observed. Some assigned an antitoxic function to the gland. Others developed a calcium relationship when it was shown that tetany was accompanied by a marked decrease of calcium in the blood. The fact that the transplantation of parathyroid glands in dogs could be carried out successfully suggested hormonal activity. Aside from suggestive work by Berman (2), Hanson (17) and some others, nothing thoroughly conclusive as evidence of a parathyroid hormone was presented until Collip arrived on the scene.

COLLIP'S WORK

In his first paper (4)[1] Collip states that success came to him when he used an extract made by acid hydrolysis of the parathyroids of the ox. With this extract he was able to control or prevent tetany in parathyroidectomized dogs. He noticed that coincidently with the clinical improvement following the use of the extract, the blood calcium level (which was very low after the operation) was raised or restored to normal. He also noticed that an overdose of the hormone gave rise to a hypercalcemia accompanied by very definite clinical symptoms.   (The blood serum calcium may rise from a normal average value of 10.5 to as high as 20 mg. per 100 cc.; and even higher.)

[1] A good historical introduction is given.

The potent extract was prepared by first grinding the fresh glands in a meat chopper, then placing the ground material in large pyrex tubes (5 by 45 cm.) and covering it with an equal volume of 5 per cent hydrochloric acid. The tubes and their contents were put in a boiling water bath from thirty minutes to one hour. During this heating the mass was stirred and broken up. The extract was now diluted with four parts of hot water and set aside to cool. The fat present congealed upon cooling and was mechanically removed. The liquid was made alkaline to pH 8 to 9 with sodium hydroxide, which dissolved practically all the suspended matter. Hydrochloric acid was now added until a maximum precipitation of protein material was obtained. This was usually found to be around pH 5.5 to 5.6. The precipitate was removed by the centrifuge (or by ordinary filtration, if rapid enough). The precipitate was redissolved in weak alkali and reprecipitated with hydrochloric acid. The filtrates were combined, and the preparation represented an aqueous solution of the active principle.

Later (6) it was found advisable to repeat the process of alkali solution and hydrochloric acid precipitation as long as any active material remains in the filtrate. This point is determined by noting whether upon making the filtrate acid to congo red and saturating it with sodium chloride, an appreciable amount of precipitate is formed. The active substance is separated from the filtrates by salting out with sodium chloride. This is done by making the solutions acid to congo red and saturating them with sodium chloride. The substance generally separates and rises to the top of the liquid. The material is filtered, dissolved in weak sodium hydroxide solution, centrifuged and the liquid adjusted to pH 4.8. The isoelectric precipitate is centrifuged off, dissolved in hydrochloric acid and the process repeated until the mother liquors are quite clear and devoid of color. The active material (A) is dissolved in hydrochloric acid at a pH of about 3, Berkefelded, standardized (see p. 29) and is then ready for use; or (A) may be dried with ether and kept in powdered form.

The extract was found effective by the oral route, by intravenous injection and by subcutaneous injection (4); though, in almost all instances, the last method was used.[2] Its effect on normal animals (13) was to elevate the level of blood serum calcium. Successive injections caused a profound hypercalcemia which, if long maintained, resulted in death.[3]

The potency of the extract was determined by injecting several normal dogs with varying amounts of it and noting the increase in blood serum calcium produced in a definite time. When calcium increase was plotted against dosage a standardization curve was obtained. The unit was defined as one one-hundredth of the amount required to produce a 5 mg. rise in blood serum calcium in 15 hours in a dog of 20 kg. (30).[4]

PREPARATION, ASSAY, AND CHEMICAL PROPERTIES OF PARATHYROID EXTRACTS

The hormone as prepared by Collip (11) (see pp. 24 and 25) can hardly be classed as a pure compound. It exhibits protein characteristics, the physical and chemical

---

[2] This view must now be revised. "All our attempts to devise some effective method of oral administration of the hormone have met with complete failure" (9).

[3] A paper by Hjort and co-workers (21), published shortly after Collip's earliest papers (that is, in 1925), very definitely confirms Collip's findings. Boiling the glands with dilute hydrochloric acid is preferable to extraction at room temperature. The active material is found in the lipoid-free fraction. Little potency is lost by removal of proteins at the isoelectric point and addition of alcohol up to 80 per cent.

[4] Though this unit is usually used, in a very recent paper, Collip defines the unit as "one one-hundredth the amount of extract required to produce a 50 per cent increase in the blood serum calcium over a period of 12 to 16 hours following a single subcutaneous or intramuscular injection" (10).

properties showing resemblances to insulin. In this crude state, the material is soluble in water on either side of its iso-electric point (pH 4.8 to 4.9). When salts are present in minimum amounts, the range of its precipitation zone is pH 4.6 to 5.2, with maximum flocking out at pH 4.8 to 4.9. The hormone is completely removed from acid solution by half saturation with ammonium sulfate or complete saturation with sodium chloride. It gives the common protein tests. The Molisch, and the orcinol-hydrochloric acid (pentose) tests are negative. Sulfur and iron are present, but phosphorus is absent. It gives precipitates with picric and picrolonic acids. It is slightly soluble in absolute alcohol, quite soluble in 80 per cent alcohol, and insoluble in ether, acetone and pyridine. Boiling one hour with either 10 per cent hydrochloric acid or 5 per cent sodium hydroxide destroys its physiological activity. Pepsin and trypsin destroy the hormone. It does not dialyze through collodion membranes. It is removed from solution by norit and Folin-Wu's tungstic acid reagent. Three-tenths milligram of the dry material is equivalent to 1 unit (for the definition of a unit, see p. 26). (See, also, (5) (6) (7) (8).)

In the preceding pages we have discussed Collip's work, which includes the preparation, assay and chemistry of the hormone. In the following paragraphs we shall provide additional information which comes to us from several laboratories.

Dodds and his co-workers (14) discovered that they could apply their picrate method (which they had used to prepare insulin (see p. 43) to prepare the parathyroid hormone. Three hundred grams of glands were extracted by the acetone-picric acid process, using the same process that they used for insulin (see p. 43), and a yield of 405 grams of hydrochloride was obtained. This was administered to rabbits, and a definite increase in serum calcium followed. The apparent similarity of insulin and parathyroid hormone is stressed.

Hanson (18) is of the opinion that the unit should be based on a treated parathyroidectomized dog, rather than upon a normal dog. Twenty-four hours after parathyroidectomy the dog will show approximately a 30 per cent drop in the blood serum calcium. Care must be taken that the animal does not show severe symptoms of tetany. An amount of extract is administered that will cause an average rise of 3 mg. in the calcium level within 6 hours, thus practically restoring the normal level. The clinical unit, in this case, is defined as one one-hundredth the amount of extract required to produce a 1 mg. rise in calcium under the specified experimental conditions. (It should be added that this unit has not been generally adopted.) In the preparation of the extract, Hanson extracts the glands with 0.5 per cent hydrochloric acid at 100°C. for about one hour. The mixture is chilled, filtered (to remove fats), and the filtrate is treated with an aqueous solution of trinitrophenol, which precipitates the active substance together with some protein. The precipitate is extracted with acetone and alcohol (containing hydrochloric acid). An excess of acetone is now added, which precipitates the active fraction. This can now be dissolved in water, diluted to the proper consistency, sterilized and prepared for clinical use, if necessary (26).

Tweedy (33) has modified Collip's method of preparing the hormone by removing inert material with acetone, precipitating the active fraction with trichloracetic acid and extracting the inert lipoidal material from this precipitate with chloroform. The fresh, frozen glands (from which as much fat as possible is removed) are ground, transferred to a conical flask, covered with 200 cc. of 3 per cent hydrochloric acid per 100 grams of gland and heated in a water bath at 70° for 20 minutes. The flask is cooled, filtered through several folds of cheese cloth (to get rid of fat), and the filtrate is brought near the neutral point but slightly on the alkaline side of Congo red, using weak sodium hydroxide. An equal volume of redistilled anhydrous acetone is added, and the mixture is set aside in the ice chest overnight. The material is now filtered through a coarse filter and evaporated *in vacuo* at 50° to one-third its volume. The residue is adjusted to the same volume as the neutralized acid extract by the addition of water and enough freshly-prepared solution of trichloracetic acid to produce a concentration of 2 per cent. The precipitate is allowed to settle overnight in the ice chest. The supernatant liquid is decanted and the residue is centrifuged, the supernatant liquid being again poured off. The precipitate is mixed with a little alcohol and dried in a desiccator *in vacuo*. It is further dried for several hours over anhydrous calcium chloride, ground and extracted with chloroform in a Soxhlet apparatus until all lipoidal material has been removed. The chloroform is removed and the residue, a gray powder, is partially or entirely soluble in 0.9 per cent sodium chloride.

If the product is not entirely water-soluble, it is suspended in 5 times its volume of acid-alcohol (15 cc. of 10 per cent hydrochloric acid to 85 cc. of 95 per cent alcohol). The fraction which is soluble in the acid-alcohol is now precipitated with ether, and the precipitate is finally washed with ether in a centrifuge. The average yield is 0.44 per cent when calculated on the basis of gross glandular weight.

For biological assay, normal dogs of either sex are used. The material, dissolved in physiological salt solution, is injected subcutaneously and blood drawn from a leg vein 15 to 16 hours later. The calcium in the blood-serum is then determined.

The product is soluble in warm 90 to 100 per cent phenol and in orthocresol. The hormone can be removed from the phenol solution either by the addition of ether or by the addition of several volumes of water. It is insoluble in anhydrous acetic acid but freely soluble in 94 per cent acid, from which it can be precipitated by the addition of

2 to 3 volumes of acetone. It is insoluble in 100 per cent pyridine, carbon tetrachloride, benzene, absolute methyl alcohol and absolute ethyl alcohol and partially soluble in glycerol at 50°C.

Acetone-dehydrated and defatted glands have been stored in a desiccator over anhydrous calcium chloride for one year without the loss of active material. The extract, prepared as just described, has been kept for 8 months without deterioration. The hormone preparation has been heated for 10 days at 100°, at the end of which time it still retains one-half its original activity.[5]

Allardyce (1), working in Collip's laboratory at McGill University, re-investigated certain points connected with the preparation of *parathormone*, as the parathyroid hormone has been called by some. In order to free the active principle from the glands, the use of acid is quite essential. Further, heating at 80° to 100°C. is found necessary in order to free the active principle as well as to destroy the enzymes present. The most potent extract is obtained by hydrolyzing the glands for 45 minutes with 1.5 per cent hydrochloric acid.

The attempts, so far, to get the hormone in a crystalline or chemically pure form have failed; and some have started with their relatively crude products to study the effect of various reagents, in the hope that some relationship might be developed between physiological activity and the presence of certain specific groups. Tweedy (34), using the active material he had already prepared (see p. 28), finds that it is inactivated by a 40 per cent aqueous solution of formaldehyde within two hours at room temperature, but that the resultant product may be partially reactivated by boiling with very dilute acetic acid for 20 minutes. This suggests the importance of NH_2 or NH groups. Inactivation with nitrous acid also suggests the importance of amino or imino groups. The hormone is adsorbed by permutit and released from it

[5] For further details of clinical assay, see (25).

by 5 per cent ammonium hydroxide at 0° to 2°C. (see, also, (31)).

It must be evident by now that our knowledge of the chemistry of the parathyroid hormone is pitifully meager. Nor are we in a position to state just what relation exists between the parathyroid hormone and vitamin D. (See, further, (31) (15) (6) (30) (35).) If the rat be substituted for the dog, we find that the former rapidly develops an apparent immunity to parathyroid extracts. However, by the injection of doses of 5 to 20 units daily, it is possible to produce an increased serum calcium and an increased excretion of calcium in the urine and feces. When, however, rats are given irradiated ergosterol, in doses of 20,000 to 50,000 units daily, there is, to be sure, an increased excretion of calcium in the urine, but it is accompanied by a decreased excretion in the feces. Animals are also responsive to irradiated ergosterol when they are almost completely immune (in so far as calcium excretion is concerned) to parathyroid hormone. "If large doses of irradiated ergosterol do stimulate parathyroid secretion," writes Pugsley (27), "this is but a small part of their pharmacological action." The increase in serum calcium and urine calcium which results from the injection of parathyroid extracts takes place very largely at the expense of the calcium stores in the bones. It is Selye's contention (29) that the parathyroid hormone directly stimulates cellular elements in the bone to increased osteoclastic activity. However, when rats previously given the hormone are next given an overdosage of it, the result is not the formation of osteoclasts and bone resorption (as in normal animals), but actually a formation of osteoblasts. Selye finds that very small doses of parathyroid hormone stimulate osteoblast formation; which may explain "parathyroid hormone immunity."

That the increase of calcium in the blood, which may result from the administration of vitamin D or from parathyroid hormone, is a phenomenon dependent upon both the hormone and the vitamin, is possible. Hess (19) has found that latent tetany, manifested by calcium concentration of about 6 mg. per 100 cc. of serum, can be brought about in a monkey by means of a low calcium diet. It is possible to raise the calcium level to 11 mg. by the oral administration of large amounts of irradiated ergosterol. If, however, the parathyroids are first extirpated, the calcium cannot be increased above 7 mg. per 100 cc. Hyperplasia of the parathyroid glands occurs in animals kept upon a diet deficient in calcium. It has been shown that chicks grown in light from which the "vital rays" have been removed exhibit a hyperplasia of the parathyroids (20). (See, also, (28) (9) and (10).)

The possible clinical applications of the parathyroid hormone are discussed in the following: (6) (28) (23) (22) (24) (9).

REFERENCES

(1) ALLARDYCE, W. J.: The chemistry and physiology of the parathyroid hormone. *Am. J. Physiol.*, **98**, 417 (1931).

(2) BERMAN, L.: The effect of a protein-free acid-alcohol extract of the parathyroid glands upon the calcium content of the blood. *Am. J. Physiol.*, **75**, 358 (1926).

(3) BOYD, J. D., MILGRAM, J. E. AND STEARNS, G.: Clinical hyperparathyroidism. *J. Am. Med. Assoc.*, **93**, 684 (1929).

(4) COLLIP, J. B.: The extraction of a parathyroid hormone which will prevent or control parathyroid tetany and which regulates the blood calcium. *J. Biol. Chem.*, **63**, 395 (1925).

(5) COLLIP, J. B.: A parathyroid hormone and its physiological action. *Annals Clin. Med.*, **4**, 219 (1925).

(6) COLLIP, J. B.: The parathyroid glands. Harvey Lectures, 1925–1926 (Williams & Wilkins, Baltimore).

(7) COLLIP, J. B.: The calcium mobilizing hormone of the parathyroid glands. *J. Am. Med. Assoc.*, **88**, 565 (1927).

(8) COLLIP, J. B.: Darstellung und Auswertung des Hormons der Nebenschilddrüsen. In *Handbuch der biolog. Arbeitsmethoden*, **5**, 803 (1928).

(9) COLLIP, J. B.: The physiology of the parathyroid glands. *Canadian Med. Assoc. J.*, **24**, 646 (1931).

(10) COLLIP, J. B.: The physiology of the parathyroid glands. *Western J. Sur., Obstet. and Gyn.*, Nov. 1932.

(11) COLLIP, J. B. AND CLARK, E. P.: Further studies on the parathyroid hormone. *J. Biol. Chem.*, **66**, 133 (1925).

(12) COLLIP, J. B. AND CLARK, E. P.: The preparation, physiological properties and method of standardization of a parathyroid hormone. *Trans. Roy. Soc. Canada*, **19**, 25 (1925).

(13) COLLIP, J. B., CLARK, E. P. AND SCOTT, J. W.: The effect of parathyroid hormone on normal animals. *J. Biol. Chem.*, **63**, 439 (1925).

(14) DAVIES, D. T., DICKENS, F. AND DODDS, E. C.: Observations on the preparation, properties and source of the parathyroid hormone. *Biochem. J.*, **20**, 695 (1926).

(15) DRAGSTEDT, L. R.: The physiology of the parathyroid glands. *Physiol. Rev.*, **7**, 499 (1927).

(16) EDITORIAL: Vitamin D and the parathyroids. *J. Am. Med. Assoc.*, **94**, 1148 (1930).

(17) HANSON, A. M.: The hormone of the parathyroid glands. *Proc. Soc. Exp. Biol. and Med.*, **22**, 560 (1925).

(18) HANSON, A. M.: The standardization of parathyroid activity. *J. Am. Med. Assoc.*, **90**, 747 (1928).

(19) HESS, A. F., WEINSTOCK, M. AND RIVKIN, H.: Effect of thyroparathyroidectomy on the action of irradiated ergosterol. *Proc. Soc. Exp. Biol. and Med.*, **26**, 555 (1929).

(20) HIGGINS, G. M. AND SHEARD, C.: The parathyroid glands as influenced by selective solar radiation. *Science*, **67**, 536 (1928).

(21) HJORT, A. M., ROBINSON, S. C. AND TENDICK, F. H.: An extract obtained from the external bovine parathyroid glands capable of inducing hypercalcemia in normal and thyroparathyroprivic dogs. *J. Biol. Chem.*, **65**, 117 (1925).

(22) LEITCH, D. B.: Use of parathormone in infantile tetany. *Canadian Med. Assoc. J.*, **17**, 1321 (1927).

(23) McCANN, W. S.: Parathyroid therapy. *J. Am. Med. Assoc.*, **88**, 565 (1927).

(24) McCANN, W. S.: Diuretic action of parathyroid extract-Collip in certain edematous patients. *J. Am. Med. Assoc.*, **90**, 249 (1928).

(25) MUNCH, J. C.: Bioassays. (Williams & Wilkins, Baltimore. 1931.)

(26) New and Nonofficial Remedies. 1933. (American Med. Assoc., Chicago.)

(27) PUGSLEY, L. I.: The effect of parathyroid hormone and of irradiated ergosterol on calcium and phosphorus metabolism in the rat. *J. Physiol.*, **76**, 315 (1932).

(28) QUICK, A. J. AND HUNSBERGER, A.: Hyperparathyroidism. *J. Am. Med. Assoc.*, **96**, 745 (1931).

(29) SELYE, H.: On the stimulation of new bone-formation with parathyroid extract and irradiated ergosterol. *Endocrinology*, **16**, 547 (1932).

(30) STEWART, C. P. AND PERCIVAL, G. H.: The effect of administration of parathyroid on the serum calcium. *Quart. J. Med.*, **20**, 349 (1927).

(31) THOMSON, D. L. AND COLLIP, J. B.: The parathyroid glands. *Physiol. Rev.*, **12**, 309 (1932).
(32) THOMSON, D. L. AND PUGSLEY, L. E.: On the mechanism of parathyroid hormone action. *Am. J. Physiol.*, **102**, 350 (1932).
(33) TWEEDY, W. R.: Studies on the plasma calcium-raising principle of bovine parathyroid glands. I. A method of preparation and some observations on the yield, solubility and stability of the product. *J. Biol. Chem.*, **88**, 649 (1930).
(34) TWEEDY, W. R. AND TORIGOE, M.: Chemical studies on a parathyroid hormone. *J. Biol. Chem.*, **99**, 155 (1932).

Chapter III

INSULIN

Perhaps no more dramatic discovery in medicine has been made within the last decade than the preparation of pancreatic extracts which can be used with success in treating diabetes. This discovery was a fitting termination to a series of researches, begun by Mehring and Minkowski in 1885, which had for their object a detailed study of the relationship of the pancreas to diabetes. Mehring and Minkowski definitely established the fact that the removal of the pancreas of normal dogs is followed by a condition resembling in all respects severe diabetes mellitus in man. These scientists, and many after them, attempted the preparation of active pancreatic extracts which could be used as replacement therapy in diabetes; but with little or no success until 1921, when the Toronto group, headed by Banting, Best, Macleod, Collip and Noble, solved the problem.

BANTING AND CO-WORKERS

The experiments were begun in 1921. The first extract was obtained by ligating the pancreatic ducts of the dog and waiting for ten weeks for degeneration of the acinar tissue. What was left (which consisted of healthy islet tissue) was removed and macerated in ice-cold Ringer solution. The extract when injected definitely reduced the blood sugar. Another active extract was made from the pancreas of a dog which had been injected with secretin. A third active extract was obtained by macerating the pancreas of fetal calves (under four months development) in Ringer's solution and filtering.

Later, alcohol was substituted for Ringer's solution. The

alcoholic extract was evaporated to dryness in a warm air current and the residue dissolved in saline solution. This extract was injected (subcutaneously or intravenously) into a diabetic dog, giving rise to a marked fall in blood sugar and in the amount of sugar excreted in the urine.

The extract prepared with alcohol no longer contained trypsin (the presence of which had given so much trouble to earlier workers). The active principle was insoluble in 95 per cent alcohol, though apparently quite soluble in alcohol containing more water. With this extract a depancreatized dog was kept alive for 70 days—far longer than had ever been possible before.

Then came the very important discovery that potent extracts of the whole gland could be obtained without difficulty provided acidified alcohol was used as the extracting medium. The extracts were obtained by using equal volumes of 95 per cent alcohol and pancreas, with the addition that the alcohol contained 0.2 per cent of hydrochloric acid. The fatty substances were removed with toluene, the alcoholic extract was reduced to one-fifth its volume by distillation *in vacuo;* and the watery extract which remained, and which contained the active principle, could be sterilized by Berkefeld filtration. This extract was given to a human diabetic, with gratifying results (4) (5) (6) (8) (63).

However, the extract still contained a relatively large amount of protein; and in several instances sterile abscesses formed at the site of injection. By a process of fractional precipitation with alcohol, Collip finally prepared a purified product which could be used repeatedly (subcutaneously or intravenously) in diabetes mellitus without any bad effects (8) (63). The method of preparation developed by him depends upon the solubility of insulin in concentrations of alcohol up to 80 to 90 per cent, above which it begins to precipitate. The proteins, on the other hand, precipitate at an alcoholic concentration considerably below 90 per cent; and, in fact, much of the protein is removed in the initial extraction, where equal volumes of the minced gland and 95 per cent alcohol are used, giving, in reality, a 50 to 60 per cent alcoholic medium (62).[1]

Equal volumes of fresh minced pancreas and 95 per cent alcohol are allowed to stand for several hours, with occasional shaking, and then filtered. Two volumes of 95 per cent alcohol are added to the filtrate. At this stage much of the protein is precipitated, but the insulin still remains in solution. The precipitate is allowed to settle for several hours, the mixture is filtered, and the filtrate is evaporated to a small volume by distillation *in vacuo* at a temperature of from 10° to 30°C. The lipoids are now removed by means of ether, and the aqueous extract which remains is further evaporated (*in vacuo*) to a pasty consistency. Eighty per cent alcohol is now added to the mixture, which is then centrifuged. Four layers separate out: a bottom layer of salt crystals; a saturated aqueous solution of salt above it; above this a flocculent layer of protein; and on top a layer of alcohol containing the insulin in solution. The alcohol layer is removed with a pipette and added to several volumes of 95 per cent (or, still better, absolute) alcohol. After standing for several hours, the precipitate, containing the insulin, is dissolved in water and concentrated *in vacuo* to the desired volume. The product is passed through a Berkefeld filter and is then ready for use. The extract is practically free from proteins, salts and alcohol-soluble substances and can be made isotonic and injected subcutaneously without local reaction.

Not only was all this work done within the space of one year, but a considerable amount of data bearing on the use

---

[1] Shaffer points out that his purified insulin (see p. 44) is soluble in alcoholic solutions up to 80 per cent, but only in the form of its acid or alkali salts. At reactions around its isoelectric point, it is little more soluble in dilute alcohol than in water (77).

of insulin in diabetes was collected. The average percentage of blood sugar in 90 normal rabbits was found to be 0.133. A marked fall in these values was found after the injection of insulin. This finally led to a method of assaying insulin. The unit was taken as that amount of insulin, which on subcutaneous injection, lowers the percentage of blood sugar to 0.045 within three hours in a rabbit weighing about 2 kg., and from which food has been withheld for from 16 to 24 hours.[2]

To show the effect of insulin on carbohydrate metabolism, the respiratory quotient was studied. In one case, a patient had been suffering from diabetes for six years. His diet for a few months prior to this investigation included about 10 grams of carbohydrate, with a total of 1200 calories. The total daily excretion of sugar had been 15 to 30 grams; the blood sugar was between 0.28 to 0.33 per cent; and acetone bodies were always present. On this diet the R.Q. was 0.74. Insulin was injected subcutaneously and 20 grams of cane sugar were given by mouth. Within two hours the R.Q. rose to 0.90. Similar results were obtained with other patients; and also with depancreatized dogs (8).

Striking, also, were the results obtained on the storage of glycogen in the liver. Depancreatized dogs, even when fed large amounts of sugar, show relatively small quantities of glycogen in the liver, as Minkowski had already shown. In two such dogs, which were fed large quantities of cane sugar for several days preceding death,[3] Banting and his coworkers found 0.044 to 0.047 per cent of glycogen in one dog and 1.29 to 1.35 per cent in the other. When insulin as well as sugar was given to depancreatized dogs for a few days before the animal was killed, the results varied anywhere from 4 per cent, in one instance to as high as 13.27 per cent

---

[2] But see page 50. At 0.045 per cent of blood sugar the animal goes into convulsions. The "rabbit unit," here given, is no longer used.

[3] Usually the animal dies about 12 days after the operation.

in another. This led to the conclusion that one effect of insulin is to stimulate the glycogenic function of the liver. The increased glycogen deposit, together with the increased R.Q. in the presence of insulin also led to the hypothesis that carbohydrate can be utilized in the body only after it has been converted into glycogen.

It was also observed that insulin given to sugar-fed diabetic animals causes a reduction of fat in the liver at the time when glycogen accumulates.

Acetone bodies, so persistently present in diabetics, disappear from the urine when insulin is given and remain absent so long as insulin is injected. This observation was followed by Banting and his co-workers with another in regard to the effect of insulin injection into animals suffering from various experimental procedures which give rise to hyperglycemia and glycosuria (such as puncture of the floor of the fourth ventricle of the medulla, subcutaneous injection of epinephrin and the various forms of asphyxia, including ether anesthesia). In none of these animals (fed though they were with abundant carbohydrate) was there more than a slight increase in blood sugar, provided they had been previously injected with insulin.

In the beginning of 1923, Banting and his co-workers already could report on the results of insulin treatment in the cases of 50 diabetic patients. All the patients were benefited by the treatment, though the most striking responses were obtained with children and young adults. After a treatment of two days (assuming that sufficient insulin has been given) the urine becomes free from sugar; and after three days, it becomes free from acetone bodies. "The patient becomes conscious of increasing strength before the end of the first week. Hunger is replaced by appetite, thirst is lessened, edema disappears in about 10 days, and a considerable amount of physical vigor is restored. The weight frequently increases; and this can be brought about by supplying food in excess of the caloric requirements, and with it an increased amount of insulin. One patient, aged 16, who had lost 40 pounds during three years of diabetes, gained 35 pounds in less than four months." The authors were also aware of the dangers of an overdose of insulin, with the consequent alarming drop of blood sugar below normal, and the train of clinical symptoms which follow. Relief invariably followed the administration of orange juice, or glucose with orange juice.

Because the unit of insulin originally adopted (see p. 38) is greater than that required in the treatment of certain cases of diabetes in man, the *clinical* unit was subsequently designated as one-third the physiological unit (p. 38). Since different rabbits react differently to equal doses of insulin, it became necessary to use many animals for the assay of any one sample of the hormone and then to take the average of the highest results obtained (64).   (See, further, (9) (22) (34) (68).)

SOURCES OF INSULIN

The main source still seems to be the islets of Langerhans of the mammalian pancreas; though various extracts have been obtained from plant and animal sources which are said to cause a reduction in blood sugar (see, also, pp. 62–63).   Collip has prepared several vegetable extracts which cause a reduction in blood sugar concentration. He first obtained the potent material from onions and has given the name *glucokinin* to it (see p. 62). Best and Scott have made 70 per cent alcoholic extracts of potatoes, rice, wheat, beetroot and celery, all of which had a definite effect when injected into normal rabbits.   These authors have also found an insulin-like substance in the blood of rabbits, dogs and oxen, the amount of which is reduced in the blood of diabetic dogs.   Whether this hormone, or one simulating it in properties, is present in urine, is not yet clear.   Active extracts (according to the reports) have been made from yeast,

oranges, lemons, grape-fruit, dried beans and oat bran.
Bacteria grown on an insulin-free medium are said to yield a
potent substance.   It is very doubtful, however, whether
these active plant extracts contain a substance really identical
with insulin.   Extracts active, though milder in their action
than insulin proper, have been obtained from the kidney,
spleen and skeletal muscle of the ox and dog.   A very en-
couraging source of insulin, according to Dudley, is the islet
tissue of fish, and particularly the codfish.   He states that
the yield of insulin from the codfish is about ten times as
much as that obtained from the mammalian pancreas (78).

PREPARATION OF INSULIN

An account of the pioneer work of Banting and Best, and,
more particularly of Collip (see p. 36), has already been
given.   We will now take up, in some detail, the several
methods which have been proposed for the preparation of
active extracts.

In 1923 Dudley (31) proposed a method of preparation
which, though largely based on the method outlined by Collip, suggests several new possibilities; among them, the purification of the hormone in the form of its picrate and also its
hydrochloride.   Five kilograms of fresh ox pancreas are
minced and added to 5 liters of 95 per cent alcohol at −3°C.
The mixture is allowed to stand for two hours and is then
filtered.   The residue is further pressed out.   The combined
filtrates amount to 5.5 liters.   One and one-half volumes of
95 per cent alcohol are added to the filtrate and the mixture
is placed overnight in the cold room at −3°C.   The mixture
is next filtered and the filtrate is evaporated *in vacuo* at 45°C.
to 250 cc.   The fat in this concentrate is extracted with
light petroleum, and the aqueous solution which is left is
made up to 80 per cent alcohol by the use of absolute alcohol.
The mixture is allowed to stand overnight in the cold room,
and the supernatant liquid is decanted and made up to 93

per cent alcohol by the addition of two volumes of absolute alcohol. The product is again placed in the cold room for 15 to 20 hours, and the precipitate which has formed and settled in the meantime is washed first with absolute alcohol and then with ether. The precipitate is dried in a vacuum desiccator over sulfuric acid. The yield is 3 to 4 grams. Five to 10 mg. of this material produces convulsions in a rabbit weighing 2 kg.

Over 50 per cent of this "crude insulin" (A) represents inorganic salts, such as chlorides and phosphates. The hormone can be precipitated from an aqueous solution of (A) by means of uranium acetate or phosphotungstic acid; but still better, by picric acid, which removes the hormone quantitatively. The picrate, which is an amorphous yellow powder, weighs from one-twelfth to one-fourteenth as much as the starting material (A). The picrate is but slightly soluble in water but dissolves in $N/15$ Na_2HPO_4. The rabbit unit is about 1 mg. The picrate can be converted into the hydrochloride by grinding the former with absolute alcohol, adding a small amount of alcoholic hydrochloric acid, stirring and finally adding ether. The hydrochloride separates out in the form of a white powder. The rabbit unit at this stage represents as little as 0.5 to 1 mgm. of the dry material.

The hydrochloride, unlike the "crude insulin," is free from organically-combined phosphorus. The Millon reaction is faint. The tryptophane test is negative. The Molisch, the biuret, the Pauly and the organic sulfur tests are all positive. The hormone is destroyed by trypsin and pepsin. Of course, we are still dealing with a highly impure product.

We have referred to Dudley's observation that the cod fish is a good source of insulin (p. 41). Dudley has here applied his picric acid method for the preparation of the hormone (32). Immediately after the fish are caught the islet tissues from 108 fish, weighing 9.6 grams in the moist state, are detached and added to a saturated aqueous picric acid solution. The picric acid is poured off, the tissue residue is cut up and ground with sand and returned to the picric acid. This is filtered at the end of 24 hours, and the tissue is ground repeatedly with small amounts of acetone, each extract being filtered off. The combined filtrates are evaporated *in vacuo*. After the removal of the acetone, the picrate separates out. This precipitate is collected by centrifuging and dissolved in 5 cc. of a mixture of 75 parts of absolute alcohol and 25 parts of 3 N aqueous hydrochloric acid. The solution is centrifuged (to get rid of suspended matter) and poured into 200 cc. of acetone. The precipitated hydrochloride is filtered off, washed with acetone and ether and dried. The yield of hydrochloride is 0.126 gram. Its activity is equivalent to 1 mg. per rabbit unit. In other words, a yield of 1.17 rabbit units is obtained from each fish; or 13.12 rabbit units (practically 40 clinical units)[4] per gram of wet tissue.

Dodds and Dickens have investigated in some detail Dudley's picrate-acetone method of preparation (27) (28). The picrate is soluble in moist alcohol, moist acetone, formamide and paraldehyde; it is insoluble in water, absolute alcohol, acetone or ether. The picrate can be thrown out of its acetone solution by dilution with an equal volume of water and addition of saturated aqueous picric acid. The majority of protein picrates are insoluble in aqueous acetone. This at once gives a means of separating insulin from its accompanying protein impurities. As Dudley has shown (p. 42), it is possible to dispense with a preliminary aqueous or aqueous alcoholic extraction of the pancreas by mixing the latter directly with picric acid.

The method adopted by Dodds and Dickens is as follows: The pancreas is minced and well stirred with finely powdered picric acid (45 grams per kilogram of pancreas). The mixture is again passed through the mincer to ensure even mixing.

[4] See page 40.

(The use of solid picric acid avoids tedious filtrations at the outset and, by converting the insulin directly to the picrate, reduces the time during which tryptic reaction may occur to a minimum.)   The picrated mass is extracted three times with acetone.   Absolute acetone is used for the first extraction in sufficient quantity to make the final concentration 70 per cent.   In the succeeding extractions, aqueous acetone (70 per cent) is used in quantity equal to half the weight of pancreas taken.   The combined extracts are filtered, if necessary, and the filtrate distilled *in vacuo* until all the acetone is removed.   Upon cooling, deposits of the picrate with some fat and crystals of picric acid separate.   An equal volume of saturated aqueous picric acid is added to ensure complete precipitation.   The precipitate is washed with ether, which removes the picric acid and the fat, leaving the picrate undissolved.

The picrate is now converted into the hydrochloride using Dudley's procedure (p. 43): the picrate is dissolved in acid-alcohol by mixing 25 cc. of aqueous 3 N hydrochloric acid with 75 cc. of alcohol.   Ten to 20 cc. of this mixture are required for each gram of picrate.   The solution is centrifuged and the supernatant fluid is poured off.   The solid material at the bottom is treated with a further quantity of acid-alcohol and the operation repeated.   The hydrochloride is precipitated in the combined filtrates by the addition of 10 to 20 volumes of acetone.   The precipitate is washed with acetone until free from picric acid, and finally with ether. It is dried in a vacuum desiccator.   The product is a white, amorphous powder, the rabbit unit of which lies between 0.25 to 1 mg. [5]

Shaffer and his co-workers have developed a method of preparing insulin which, whilst it retains the use of alcohol for extraction (as suggested by Collip) introduces three important modifications: the use of strong acid during the alco-

[5] The rabbit unit has been defined on page 38.

hol extraction; the precipitation of the active substance from the crude aqueous solutions by ammonium sulfate; and the precipitation of the insulin from the semi-purified solutions by adjusting the reaction to pH 5 to 6 (29) (77). The use of strong acid insures the solution of the insulin and prevents its destruction by proteolytic enzymes. Precipitation by half saturation with ammonium sulfate causes a separation from about nine-tenths of the accompanying proteins. By precipitation of the insulin at pH 5 very active preparations are obtained.[6] The final product is a protein, giving positive biuret and Millon reactions, but a negative Hopkins-Cole. On injection into rabbits, about 0.05 mg. of dry substance per kilogram of body weight causes convulsions and marked hypoglycemia; so that, on this basis, about 0.03 mg. may be taken as 1 standard Toronto unit. (For a 2 kg. rabbit, $(0.05 \times 2) \div 3 = 0.033$ mg. for 1 unit.)

The precipitate obtained at pH 5 contains at least 3 proteins; one of these proteins has its optimum precipitation at pH 7 to 8, another has its optimum at pH 4, and the third, containing the insulin, precipitates completely at pH 5. Obviously, the two inactive proteins are incompletely precipitated at pH 5.

The preparation is carried out as follows: Fresh beef pancreas is finely hashed by passing twice through a meat grinder. Before passing the material a second time through the grinder, 20 to 30 cc. of 10 N sulfuric acid for each kilogram of hash are added to it. Fifteen hundred cubic centimeters of 95 per cent alcohol per kilogram of hash are now added. After standing at room temperature for 4 to 12 hours, with occasional stirring, the mixture is filtered. The residue is

[6] In the absence of salts, insulin precipitates between pH 4.4 and 5.8, with optimum precipitation around pH 5. In the presence of salts, the range is considerably modified. It may be mentioned at this point that Wintersteiner and Abramson have shown that the iso-electric point of crystalline insulin is between pH 5.6 and 5.65.

pressed and the press-liquid filtered. The residue is re-extracted with 60 to 70 per cent alcohol. The combined filtrates (2,100 cc. per kilogram) are evaporated at low temperature to one-tenth the volume and filtered. The precipitate is washed with water until the filtrate has a volume of 200 cc. per kilogram of pancreas used. To the filtrate (which is at pH 2.5 to 3.1) are added 40 grams of ammonium sulfate for each 100 cc. The product is allowed to stand for several hours in the ice-box, the liquid is poured off from the gummy precipitate, the latter is dissolved in water (100 cc. per kilogram of pancreatic hash) and again precipitated by the addition of two-thirds its volume of saturated ammonium sulfate solution. The product is placed in the ice-box for several hours and the liquid is poured off from the precipitate as before. The precipitate is dissolved in water containing enough 0.1 N ammonium hydroxide to make the reaction just yellow to methyl red (pH 6 to 8). At this point the insulin dissolves, but much of the protein which precipitates around pH 7 to 8 remains undissolved. The solution is centrifuged, the supernatant liquid is poured off and diluted with water (to about 100 cc. for each kilogram of pancreas). Dilute acetic acid is now added to about pH 5 (about midway of the color change of methyl red). The precipitate is allowed to stand for several hours, then centrifuged, washed with water at pH 5 and dissolved in 0.1 N acetic acid (5 to 10 cc. for each kilogram of pancreas represented by the precipitate). Twenty per cent of the equivalent of sodium hydroxide is now added. This mixture (acetic acid, one-fifth neutralized), gives a pH close to 4, at which stage the insulin is soluble, whereas the protein with the isoelectric point at 4 is insoluble. The product is allowed to remain in the cold room for some hours, then centrifuged and the precipitate is washed with a small quantity of water. The supernatant liquid is poured off and an additional amount of sodium hydroxide, corresponding exactly to one-half the

equivalent of the acetic acid used, is added. This gives a
solution of acetic acid, seven-tenths neutralized, the pH of
which is close to 5. The insulin separates out; and the precipitation is completed by keeping the material in the ice-box
for several days. The product is centrifuged, the precipitate
is washed with distilled water and dissolved by the addition
of a few drops of dilute hydrochloric acid.

Scott's method of preparing insulin (72) is not very different from Shaffer's, except in the last stages. He also extracts the pancreas with acid-alcohol (using hydrochloric
acid in the place of sulfuric acid), precipitates with ammonium sulfate, and fractionates precipitates at different acidi-
ties. But the final stage, precipitation with trichloracetic
acid, purifies the insulin still further. The final snow-white
product, when submitted to physiological assay, shows
25,000 units of insulin per gram of powder. The purification with trichloracetic acid is made by adding a concentrated
solution of the acid to a solution of insulin (dissolved in acid
water) until a concentration of 3 per cent is reached. The
insulin is completely precipitated. The precipitate is centrifuged off, dissolved in acid water and the pH adjusted to
6.2. This is allowed to stand overnight, during which time
a small precipitate settles out. The precipitate is removed
and the supernatant fluid is adjusted to pH 3.7. The precipitate which now appears is centrifuged off, and the supernatant liquid is adjusted to pH 5.0. The precipitate which
forms, and which contains the insulin, is centrifuged off and
dissolved in a small quantity of 50 per cent alcohol. The
insulin is precipitated out by adding 20 volumes of acetone. After standing overnight, the solid material is filtered
off on a hardened filter paper and then dried in a vacuum
desiccator over phosphorus pentoxide.

The method used by manufacturers to produce insulin
in quantity makes use (in at least one instance) of a combination of procedures due primarily to Collip and to Shaf-

fer. While the pancreas of any animal yields insulin, the pancreas of the hog or cattle is used for its commercial production (74). The glands are extracted with an equal volume of alcohol containing about 1 per cent of sulfuric acid. Since it is difficult to remove traces of metal from pancreatic extracts, enamelled or earthenware apparatus is used throughout the series of operations. After several hours, the material is filtered and the residue is extracted with an equal volume of 70 per cent alcohol. The alcohol is removed and the fat fraction, which then separates out, is removed by skimming and filtration (A). From now on, one of two procedures may be adopted, "without making any marked difference in the yield": precipitation with ammonium sulfate (Shaffer) or concentration with alcohol (Collip). In the former method, ammonium sulfate is added to one-half saturation, the precipitate is dissolved in acidified alcohol and the solution neutralized. The precipitated insulin fraction is further purified by dissolving in acidified water, making the solution alkaline to pH 7.3 to 7.5, removing the inert precipitate and acidifying the solution to pH 5.0, when the insulin fraction precipitates. The precipitate is redissolved in acidified water and again brought to pH 5.0 with alkali. The precipitated insulin is dissolved in acidulated water at pH 2.5, to which 0.1 per cent "tricresol" is added as a preservative and enough sodium chloride is added to make the solution isotonic with the blood. The solution is tested for its potency on rabbits, sterilized by passing it through a Berkefeld filter and put into ampules. This process is the "isoelectric precipitation method."

The alternative method, which follows Collip's procedure rather closely, is to add alcohol at point (A) until the concentration reaches 80 per cent (1). The inert material is filtered off and 5 to 6 volumes of 95 per cent alcohol are added to the filtrate—until the alcoholic concentration is 93 per cent. This precipitate, which contains practically all the insulin is dissolved in acidified water and reprecipitated at pH 5.0. This isoelectric method of precipitation is repeated 4 to 5 times. The final precipitate is taken up in a minimum quantity of acid water (hydrochloric acid). "The concentrated water solution is now evaporated to dryness and the resultant horny precipitate ground in a mortar . . . . In drying the material, it is placed in glass trays in very thin layers and evaporated at a low temperature (in a high vacuum or at a low temperature with a current of air. It is preferable to use the vacuum)." The material is obtained as the hydrochloride (1).

Blatherwick and his associates (15), in preparing insulin, have used a combination of the procedures of Shaffer and of Scott. They use sodium chloride instead of ammonium sulfate as a precipitant, first, because less salt is required, and secondly, because it is convenient to use when nitrogen studies are to be made, and thirdly, because there is no danger of introducing sulfates when a study of the sulfur content of insulin is being made. Phenol (to a concentration of 0.2 per cent) is used as a preservative and enough sodium chloride is also added to make the solution isotonic. The liquid is drawn through a Mandler filter and bottled. "Such preparations appear to keep indefinitely at room temperature without loss of potency." The yield varies from 1800 to 2500 clinical units per kilogram of pancreas. Further purification of the insulin is possible by fractional precipitation with alcohol.

Gerlough and Bates (45) have modified Scott's method of preparation at the stage of the ammonium sulfate precipitation. The insulin precipitated by ammonium sulfate is defatted with an alcohol-ether mixture (1:5), dried and then dispersed as completely as possible in one-fifteenth of its original volume of water. The reaction is maintained at pH 2.5 to 2.8. The crude insulin is again salted out, this time by the addition of 16 grams of anhydrous sodium sulfate for each 100 cc. The precipitate (which rises to the top) is removed and drained. One thousand grams of this wet precipitate is taken up with water and alcohol to make 7 liters of 60 per cent by volume. The insoluble precipitate is centrifuged off, dispersed in water and extracted with 3.5 liters of 60 per cent alcohol. The precipitate is again centrifuged off and re-extracted a third time. A very small amount of insulin remains in the insoluble material. All of the extracts are combined and precipitated in 90 to 92 per cent alcohol. The precipitate is washed with ether, dried and then taken up with water and reprecipitated three times isoelectrically at pH 5.0 to remove salts and inert, soluble protein.

INSULIN ASSAY

The standardization of insulin has already been referred to (pp. 38 and 40). The unit (clinical) of insulin has been taken as one-third of the amount required to lower the blood sugar of a normal rabbit, weighing 2 kg. and previously fasted for two hours, to the convulsive level within three hours. The international standard, now generally accepted, has been prepared by Dudley as follows (67): Sodium carbonate is added to the "commercial" insulin solution (in dilute hydrochloric) until the development of turbidity ("isoelectric point"). A saturated aqueous solution of picric acid is added until no further precipitation occurs. The precipitate is washed and dissolved in a mixture of nine parts of alcohol and one part of concentrated aqueous hydrochloric acid. The solution is centrifuged, to remove insoluble material, and poured into dry acetone. The precipitate of insulin hydrochloride is washed with acetone and ether (to remove excess picric acid) and dried *in vacuo* over sulfuric acid. Assays of a mixed lot showed a potency of somewhat over 8 (clinical) units per milligram. To avoid fractions, the powder was said to contain 8 units per milligram. The

definition of an international unit is therefore the quantity
of a given preparation which produces an effect on carbohydrate metabolism equal to 0.125 mg. of the international
standard preparation of dry insulin hydrochloride. (See, also,
(69) (63).)

PROPERTIES OF INSULIN

One must be very careful in the interpretation of results
at this point, because it is well known how the properties
of the hormone vary with the state of its purity. This, of
course, applies to all physiological extracts, and unless one
deals with pure products, such as adrenaline or thyroxine,
the properties of the active material must be considered in
relation to the method by which the active material has been
prepared.[7] In a general way, however, it may be stated
that insulin is soluble in water and in alcohol up to 80 per
cent, provided the solution is not at the "isoelectric point"
(around pH 5.0), and that it is insoluble in alcohol above 90
per cent and in fat solvents in general. It is unstable when
heated for a short time at pH 4.0. Widmark (83), who used
the "crude insulin" of Collip and of Shaffer, prepared in
1922–1923, states that his product is practically insoluble in
carbon tetrachloride, ethyl acetate, ethyl alcohol, isobutyl
alcohol, amyl alcohol, chloroform, acetone, light petroleum,
ethyl ether, benzene, xylene, and pyridine. It is easily
soluble in methyl alcohol, glacial acetic acid, phenol and
formamide. Since methyl alcohol, phenol and formamide
are solvents for proteoses, Widmark argues in favor of the view
that insulin is a proteose. The "crude insulin" gives positive
biuret and xanthoproteic tests; it gives a precipitate with
nitric acid which disappears on boiling; it is not precipitated
on boiling; it is precipitated from water solution by half
saturation with ammonium sulfate; it is easily destroyed by

[7] The properties enumerated at this point are still not necessarily those
of "pure" or "crystalline" insulin.

trypsin; and it cannot be dialyzed through parchment membranes nor "ultrafiltered" through 3 per cent collodion filters.

Further properties are recorded by Shonle and Waldo (75), of the Eli Lilly Laboratories, where much of the large-scale production of the hormone was undertaken. The "crude insulin" is precipitated by tungstic, phosphotungstic, nitric, trichloracetic, tannic, picric and m-phosphoric acids. It is also precipitated by zinc sulfate as well as by sodium and ammonium sulfates. By repeated precipitation at the isoelectric point or with trichloracetic acid, it becomes possible to obtain a preparation containing a minimum amount of nitrogen and which is practically free from non-protein nitrogen. (But continued reprecipitation also destroys some of the active material.) One cubic centimeter of the purified preparation, containing 100 units, gives a negative Molisch reaction (carbohydrate); a positive biuret reaction (protein); a faint ninhydrin reaction (α-amino-acid group); a negative Hopkins-Cole reaction (tryptophane); a negative Ehrlich p-dimethylaminobenzaldehyde reaction (indole derivatives); a faint Millon reaction (tyrosine); a positive Ehrlich diazo reaction (tyrosine and histidine); a positive xanthoproteic reaction (benzene nucleus); a positive reaction for cystine and tyrosine by Folin's method (*J. Biol. Chem.*, **51**, 421 (1922)); a positive test for reduced sulfur after boiling with sodium hydroxide; no color reaction with sodium nitroprusside (—SH groups); no phosphorus test after fusion; and after hydrolysis, a negative Wheeler-Johnson reaction (uracil and cytosine) and no precipitate with ammoniacal silver nitrate (purines). The destruction of the physiological activity does not affect any of these reactions.

Precipitation methods are inadequate to purify insulin to the point of securing a substance of constant composition: the same methods of purification on different lots yield products showing a marked variation in the C, H and N content. This, however, is not true with crystalline insulin;

here the composition does not vary with different lots of crystals.

Purified insulin is soluble in dilute acids and alkalis, but is insoluble at a pH 4.7 to 5.0. ("Crude insulin," which is water-soluble, can be purified so that the entire activity is retained by a fraction insoluble in water.) It is unstable towards alkali but relatively stable towards acids. It is soluble in acidified absolute alcohol and in dilute alkaline alcohol. Two and one-half per cent trichloracetic acid precipitates 95 per cent of the activity of the insulin.

Insulin is not only destroyed by trypsin, but also by pepsin, erepsin and papain.[8] It is adsorbed by kaolin, charcoal and Lloyd's reagent. With the last, the amount adsorbed is proportional to the amount of proteose adsorbed. It is precipitated (together with the proteose) by both positive and negative colloids. Prolonged dialysis of purified insulin causes from 10 to 20 per cent of the activity to pass into the dialysate. (Compare this with Widmark, p. 51.)

Insulin is destroyed by oxidation with very dilute solutions of hydrogen peroxide or potassium permanganate. Reducing agents such as sodium bisulfite, sulfur dioxide, hydrogen and stannous chloride destroy the activity. "The pancreatic substance containing insulin," write the authors, "appears to be a complex mixture of proteoses . . . . "Insulin may be a protein possessing specific physiological activity or it may consist of a chemical complex attached to a protein molecule" (75).

The preparation by Scott (72), which is described on page 47, shows characteristic protein reactions. (The chemical tests were done on a purified insulin solution containing 100 units per cubic centimeter.) The color reactions for tryptophane are faint. Phosphorus is not present. The Molisch and orcein tests are negative. The carbon and

[8] Under certain conditions, the insulin which is inactivated by trypsin may be partly reactivated (71); but this has been denied by Freudenberg.

hydrogen values obtained as a result of a combustion analysis are within the limits of those obtained for a typical protein, though the nitrogen value is somewhat low. Benzoyl chloride and carbon disulfide inactivate insulin in an alkaline solution; formaldehyde and nitrous acid greatly decrease its activity.

Insulin is slowly destroyed by boiling with 0.25 per cent sulfuric acid and rapidly destroyed by boiling in a solution barely alkaline (pH 8.6 to 9.0) (74).

Insulin can be inactivated by ethyl alcohol and hydrochloric acid, and the activity completely recovered by treatment with aqueous sodium hydroxide (18). Using insulins of different degrees of purity (including Abel's crystalline insulin (see p. 55) with a potency of 24 units per milligram), Bischoff (13) finds that concentrated sulfuric acid, at a low temperature, dissolves the hormone and renders it water-insoluble at a pH more acid than 4.8. Half of the potency is retained. Cyanide and dimethyl sulfate (in concentrated sulfuric acid) do not make the product less active; but formalin completely destroys the activity. Nitrite "in several instances" produces a biuret-free product, retaining half the original potency.

Scott finds that crystalline insulin can withstand a temperature of $-50°C$. without its physiological activity being destroyed (73). The insulin prepared by Gerlough and Bates (see p. 49), which yields a product as potent as crystalline insulin (p. 55), is apparently devoid of tryptophane (45). Employing his ultracentrifugal methods, Svedberg has determined the molecular weight of crystalline insulin (76); he finds it to be 35,100. "The molecular weight, sedimentation constant, molar frictional constant and molecular radius of insulin are within the limits of error identical with the corresponding constants for egg albumin and Bence-Jones protein. These circumstances make it extremely probable that insulin is a well-defined protein and that the physiological activity of this hormone is a property of the insulin molecule itself or some special group within it."

Funk finds that a purified insulin preparation gives with flavianic acid ("Naphtolgelb S") a compound of constant composition (43). This compound can be converted into insulin flavianate-picrate, then into picrate, hydrochloride and finally into insulin in a pure state. In a later communication (44), the conversion of insulin into two active substances is announced.

THE CHEMISTRY OF INSULIN

This section is more or less a continuation of the preceding paragraphs, because obviously the "properties" and the "chemistry" of insulin are too intimately connected to be sharply separated.

The study of the structure of the insulin molecule has become possible largely through the isolation of crystalline insulin by Abel and his co-workers; for though the evidence is not yet conclusive, it is at present generally taken for granted that crystalline insulin represents a pure substance. In the development of these difficult studies, Jensen, Geiling, Rouiller, Wintersteiner, du Vigneaud—to name but a few—have taken a leading part.

In his first communication Abel (1) describes a method for purifying commercial insulin by using pyridine and phenol. The insulin is first precipitated with $N/6$ pyridine, and redissolved in $N/6$ acetic acid. This operation is repeated 5 to 6 times. In this way, 35 to 40 per cent of inactive material is removed. The final precipitate obtained with pyridine is dissolved in 90 per cent phenol. The addition of much water now precipitates the hormone. The precipitate is dissolved in $N/6$ acetic acid and again precipitated with $N/6$ pyridine solution. The precipitate is dissolved in water (containing $N/6$ acetic acid) and reprecipitated by the addition of a saturated solution of sodium chloride. This is dissolved in acidulated (acetic acid) water and precipitated with $N/6$ pyridine.   The process is repeated until all of the sodium chloride has been removed (A).

In one of his next publications, Abel (2) describes his method of obtaining crystalline insulin.   One gram of the purified fraction (A) is dissolved in a little more than the minimum quantity of $N/6$ acetic acid, enough water is added to bring the volume up to 60 cc., and the contaminating substances, together with some insulin, are precipitated by the addition of an acidulated solution of brucine (6 grams of brucine in 95 cc. of $N/6$ acetic acid).   The product is centrifuged, and the supernatant liquid withdrawn and $N/6$ pyridine added to it.   The product is immediately centrifuged. "The precipitate which settles out is largely crystalline in character, the sides of the tube are found to be coated with glistening highly refractive crystals and the topmost layer of the precipitate consists of similar crystals."

This crystalline insulin is free from phosphorus but contains 3.2 per cent of sulfur (48).   It responds to the usual protein tests.   Its physiological activity corresponds to 24 international units per milligram, which is as high as that obtained by any investigator, except Dingemanse, who claims to have obtained an amorphous variety four times as active(24); but this is still questioned (80) (51).   Dingemanse prepares her active material by first getting rid of accompanying impurities with $N/100$ sodium bicarbonate. The residue is dissolved in $N/100$ hydrochloric acid and shaken with activated charcoal.   The carbon adsorbs the insulin and some 75 per cent of the impurities remain behind. The insulin is next extracted with 80 per cent phenol and the phenol extract is considerably diluted with water to precipitate the insulin.   (The procedure at this stage follows closely the method outlined by Abel.)   The product is purified by repeated adsorption with carbon and elution with phenol.

An improved method of getting insulin crystals is as

follows (2a): 2.001 grams of crude insulin are dissolved in 20 cc. of a 10 per cent acetic acid solution. Eighty cubic centimeters of a solution of 1 gram of brucine to each 18 cc. of $N/6$ acetic acid, and 40 cc. of a 13.5 per cent solution of pyridine, are added slowly and with stirring. The precipitate is removed by centrifuging, the supernatant liquid is withdrawn, and to it is added 40 cc. of a 0.65 per cent solution of ammonia (in small quantities at a time). The precipitate which may form is removed by centrifuging and the clear (or cloudy) fluid (which is near the isoelectric point of insulin, pH 5.5 to 5.6) is set aside to crystallize. In 24 hours the sides and bottom of the flask are found lined with glistening crystals. (The brucine serves to hold the insulin in solution and also holds in solution a considerable amount of impurities.)

Harington has devised what he considers an improvement over Abel's method of preparing the crystalline hormone (46). He makes use of a discovery that the properties of commercial insulin (or shall we say the solubility of the hormone?) are modified by the presence in solution of an active saponin. Insulin in dilute acetic acid, containing about 1 per cent saponin, is treated gradually with ammonia. At pH 5.6, after standing, the precipitate which forms is partly crystalline. The hormone is recrystallized by isoelectric precipitation from phosphate buffer solution, but this time without the aid of saponin. Harington tested physiologically four sets of insulin crystals, two prepared by Abel's methods and two by his own. "The impressive consistency of the results is evidence of the identity of the compound with insulin." The average physiological activity for each sample, using the international standard, was 23.3. Not only were uniform results obtained with crystals obtained from different sources and in different ways, but the crystals themselves represented a clearly defined structure; all of which speaks in favor of the identity of the crystals with the hormone itself.

In the attempt to gather still further evidence that the crystals and the hormone are identical, Jensen and his associates, working in Abel's laboratory, prepared crystalline insulin from the islets of the codfish and the pollock and compared the properties of the hormone so obtained with those of the hormone obtained from other sources (55). The islet tissue of the codfish and the pollock (about 1000 islets) are thrown at once into 95 per cent alcohol, containing 1 per cent of hydrochloric acid. The material is filtered at the end of three hours and the residue is re-extracted twice with acid-alcohol. The alcohol from the combined filtrates is removed, and the fat is extracted with ether. The aqueous residue is filtered, the filtrate is evaporated to a small volume and then filtered again and extracted with ether. Thirteen and one-half per cent of pyridine is now added to the remaining filtrate to throw out the insulin, and the mixture is allowed to stand overnight in the ice-box. If no precipitate forms, the aqueous solution is evaporated still further and pyridine added again. The precipitate is centrifuged and washed with alcohol and ether. From this product crystals are obtained by applying Abel's technique (2a), described on page 56.

From 1000 islets about 50 mg. of crystals can be obtained. The product gives the usual protein tests and the sulfur content (3.15 per cent) is comparable to that found in crystalline beef insulin. The physiological assay yields about 25 international units per milligram. In shape, in physiological activity and in sulfur content, these crystals are identical with those prepared from beef insulin.

Hydrolysis of the crystalline insulin material has so far failed to reveal the presence in the hydrolytic products of anything but amino acids. The first study (81) showed that cystine and tyrosine could be isolated. Then followed the evidence that arginine, histidine, leucine and possibly lysine were also present (56). Glutamic acid was next isolated

(53). An analysis on a 4-gram sample of crystalline insulin (54) gave the following figures (per cent): tyrosine, 12; cystine, 12; glutamic acid, 21; leucine, 30; arginine, 3; histidine, 8; lysine, 2 (49). The presence of proline and valine was doubtful. "No evidence of the occurrence of aspartic acid, hydroxyglutamic acid, glycine, or of any constituent foreign to the protein molecule has been obtained."

In the attempt to link the physiological activity to certain amino acid groups (48), derivatives of insulin have been prepared and studied. With acetic anhydride, insulin forms acetyl insulin, which is far less active (about one-fifth), physiologically, than the hormone itself. The acetyl insulin can be hydrolyzed, presumably to give back the insulin; but the product so obtained, even though it shows an activity higher than the acetylated compound, is nevertheless lower than the original insulin (about one-half). However, it suggests the probable importance of the groups —OH,—NH$_2$ and =NH (with which groups acetylation would take place) (50) (37) (40). Insulin dissolved in $M/15$ Na$_2$HPO$_4$ combines with benzaldehyde to form an inactive product, which, so far, has defied re-activation (51) (41). Complete inactivation of insulin is obtained by treatment with ethyl alcohol and hydrochloric acid; and complete recovery of potency is obtained by treatment with dilute sodium hydroxide (18) (41). Some ascribe this reaction to the "blocking" of the —OH, —NH$_2$ or =NH group by ethylation, and others to the esterification of the —COOH group.

Insulin gives no positive test for the sulfhydryl group and it is assumed that the sulfur is present in the disulfide or cystine linkage. There is some evidence for this view. Mild reducing agents such as cysteine and glutathione reduce the disulfide linkage in insulin and give a product which is inactive and which cannot be reactivated. Initial inactivation, however, coincides with the first appearance of a sodium nitroprusside test for the —SH group (48).

When insulin is heated with $N/10$ hydrochloric acid in a boiling water bath a coagulum is obtained which is physiologically inactive; the activity may be restored by treating the coagulum with dilute alkali. That physiologically important groups are involved in this reaction is probable, but just which groups is not so clear (40) (41). The action of alkali on the hormone splits off sulfur and ammonia, the product formed being inactive. There is some correlation between the degree of inactivation and the amount of ammonia split off. Jensen is of the opinion that the sulfur is a part of the active grouping, though this is denied by Freudenberg (48) (56) (41) (40).

Jensen has proposed the following structures (composed, wholly or in part, of glutamic acid and cystine) to represent the characteristic constituent of the insulin molecule (48):

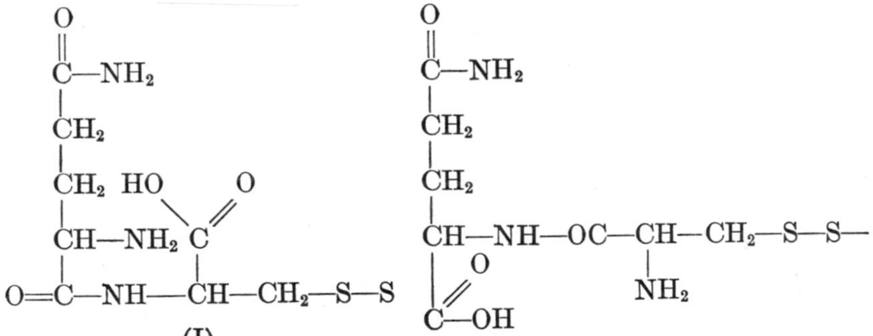

(I)

This is, of course, a mere working hypothesis for the time being. Cystine, can be supposed to be in combination with some amino acid other than glutamic; but cystine itself, in Jensen's view, is important. (See, further, (25) (38) (39) (26) (60) (80) (51) (52) (49) (42) (45) (79).)

Solutions of crystalline insulin are levorotatory. When heated, the crystals begin to brown at 215°C. and melt sharply (with decomposition) at 233°C.

Trypsin (without kinase) and aminopolypeptidase or di-

peptidase do not affect the protein structure of insulin and the
activity of the latter remains unchanged.   Pepsin, trypsin-
kinase and papain do hydrolyze insulin, and with it the
activity of the hormone disappears.

The reduction of insulin gives an inactive product which
has so far not been re-activated.   Oxidizing reagents produce
similar results.

Alkali splits off ammonia and sulfur.   "There is evidence
that inactivation results through hydrolysis of certain pep-
tide linkages .... Irreversible inactivation is always accompanied by a decrease in cystine sulfur .... Although the
groupings attacked by the various reagents are by no means
exactly known, it is still suggestive that the amino group is
probably attacked in most cases.   The isolation of glutamic
acid from insulin and the similarity of the physiological rôle
of insulin to that of glutathione as an activator of certain metabolic processes, suggests that glutamine is a constituent of
the active group" (49a).

INSULIN IN BLOOD AND IN URINE

Best and Scott (10) have reported the presence in the blood
of various animals of a substance which they believe to be
insulin.   Under certain conditions, they claim, this hormone
is eliminated in the urine.   The equivalent of 800 cc. of normal urine when injected into a pancreatectomized dog showed
the following results: beginning, 0.229 per cent blood sugar;
in 3 hours after injection, 0.210 per cent; in 5 hours, 0.171
per cent; in 9 hours, 0.104 per cent; in 11 hours, 0.079 per
cent.   Brugsch (17) confirms these findings.   On the other
hand, Watson (82) records experiments which tend to show
that there is a substance present in urine which causes
partial inactivation of insulin when the urine and insulin are
mixed, incubated, and the effect of the injection of the resultant product on blood sugar observed.   In any case, the
lowering of the blood sugar, if there is a lowering, is not sufficiently specific.

PHYSIOLOGICAL AND CLINICAL APPLICATIONS

The book (66) and article (65) by Macleod, and the book (57) by Joslin may be suggested.   Several further references are (69) (23) (78) (64) (63).

INSULIN-LIKE SUBSTANCES IN TISSUES OTHER THAN THE PANCREAS

(See p. 40.) Collip early propounded the view that wherever glycogen occurs in nature, a substance somewhat analogous to that produced by the pancreas of higher animals would be found (19).   Clam tissue was first investigated and extracts were obtained which produced marked hypoglycemia in rabbits.   Extracts made from the green tops of young onions produced hypoglycemia in normal rabbits and a marked fall in the blood sugar of a depancreatized dog.   Active extracts were later prepared from lettuce leaves, young wheat grass, young bean tops, barley roots and sprouted grain.   That these plant extracts are definitely different, however, from pancreatic extracts is brought out by the fact that with the former, the depression of the level of blood sugar in the normal rabbit is not seen until some hours, or in some instances until some days, after the injection has been made; which is in marked contrast to the immediate action of injected insulin.   The name *glucokinin* is suggested for the hormone-like substance of plant origin.

In the preparation of the material, the tissue is made permeable by autoclaving for 20 minutes at a steam pressure of 5 pounds.   The tissue is transferred to a press and the sap expressed.   A fairly effective crude extract may be made by adding two volumes of acetone to the sap.   The material is filtered, and the filtrate is concentrated to the desired degree.   The active principle can also be precipitated from the fresh sap by means of ammonium sulfate (21) (20).

A totally depancreatized dog was kept alive 66 days with injections of onion extract.

Best and Scott (10) have obtained insulin-like action with extracts from the submaxillary, thymus and thyroid glands, and liver, spleen and muscle tissue.

Winter (47) has prepared an anti-diabetic hormone from yeast, using Dudley's picric acid method of extraction.

Allen (3) has prepared an extract from the blueberry green leaves, to which he has given the name *myrtillin*, which can be given by mouth to diabetics and reduces their glycosuria. The myrtillin is prepared by air-drying the leaves and extracting the dried material for several hours at 70°C. with 50 per cent alcohol (slightly acidified with hydrochloric acid). The material is filtered, "and 95 per cent alcohol is added in sufficient quantity for the precipitation and removal of the proteins present." Addition of a 20 per cent solution of ammonium sulfate to the alcoholic filtrate precipitates the impure myrtillin.

SYNTHALIN

The fact that the action of insulin is destroyed when given by mouth has led chemists and physiologists to look for substitutes which might be effective when given orally. Perhaps the best-known of these, so far, is *synthalin*, a guanidine derivative said to be dekamethylenediguanidine (57),

$$HN=C\underset{NH-(CH_2)_{10}-NH}{\overset{NH_2}{\diagup}}C=NH \quad \overset{H_2N}{\diagdown}$$

which when given by mouth reduces the sugar in the blood and in the urine. It was first tried by Frank and his associates (36) in Minkowski's clinic in Breslau, who found that the substance definitely alleviates diabetic symptoms. Its action is slower and more lasting than that of insulin. Because of its slow action the authors have not ventured to use it in diabetic coma. They are also aware of the somewhat toxic nature of the substance, and they therefore suggest that doses be increased very gradually. The nature of this "toxicity" has been investigated in several laboratories. Blatherwick (16) has compared the action of synthalin with that of hydrazine (which had been studied by Lewis). The hypoglycemia produced by hydrazine is accompanied by an increased amount of amino-acids in the blood. The primary cause of this hypoglycemia is failure of normal glycogenesis, the transformation of non-carbohydrate materials to glucose, as a result of which the supply of glucose available is diminished because of the hepatic injury produced by hydrazine (61). Blatherwick finds that hydrazine and synthalin both interfere with deaminization, but the former seems to cause a more severe injury to this mechanism. He is of the opinion that the hypoglycemia produced by synthalin may be due to a combination of at least two processes: one of these resembles the action of insulin and the other that of hydrazine. The latter substance appears to cause hypoglycemia by injuring the liver. Synthalin interferes with this mechanism but to a lesser degree. Insulin has no such inhibiting effect.[9]

It is believed that the structure

$$H_2N-C \underset{\underset{H}{\overset{|}{N}}-(CH_2)_n-N<}{\overset{NH}{\diagup}}$$

is an important one in all hypoglycemic guanidine compounds, of which synthalin, so far, is the most active (14) (11). (See, also, (33) (70).) Neither myrtillin nor synthalin is at present used clinically.

---

[9] *Glukhormont*, used by Von Noorden and others, is considered by Bischoff to be a guanidine derivative of the *synthalin* type (12).

INTARVIN

This odd-carbon synthetic fat was produced by Kahn (59) to counteract the production of acetone bodies in diabetes. The *intarvin* (the name given to the C_{17} fatty acid) was prepared by distilling the calcium salts of stearic and acetic acids and oxidizing the resulting ketone. Dakin's theory of β-oxidation suggests that only fatty acids with an even number of carbon atoms can be the source of the acetone bodies. Since the natural fats all contain an even number of carbon atoms, Kahn therefore produced a synthetic fat with an odd number of carbon atoms. *Intarvin* has the advantage of being active when given by mouth; but for reasons which are not altogether clear, it has not come into general use.

REFERENCES

(1) ABEL, J. J., AND GEILING, E. M. K.: Researches on insulin. I. Is insulin an unstable sulfur compound? *J. Pharmacol.*, **25**, 423 (1925).

(2) ABEL, J. J.: Crystalline insulin. *Proc. Nat. Acad. Sciences*, **12**, 132 (1926).

(2a) ABEL, J. J., GEILING, E. M. K., ROUILLER, C. A., BELL, F. K., AND WINTERSTEINER, O.: Crystalline insulin. *J. Pharmacol.*, **31**, 65 (1927).

(3) ALLEN, F. M.: Blueberry leaf extract. Physiologic and clinical properties in relation to carbohydrate metabolism. *J. Am. Med. Assoc.*, **89**, 1577 (1927).

(4) BANTING, F. G., AND BEST, C. H.: The internal secretion of the pancreas. *J. Lab. and Clin. Med.*, **7**, 251 (1922).

(5) BANTING, F. G., AND BEST, C. H.: Pancreatic extracts. *J. Lab. and Clin. Med.*, **7**, 464 (1922).

(6) BANTING, F. G., BEST, C. H., COLLIP, J. B., CAMPBELL, W. R., AND FLETCHER, A. A.: Pancrea'ic extracts in the treatment of diabetes mellitus. *Canadian Med. Assoc. J.*, **12**, 141 (1922).

(7) BANTING, F. G., BEST, C. H., COLLIP, J. B, MACLEOD, J. J. R., AND NOBLE, E. C.: The effect of pancreatic extract (insulin) on normal rabbits. *Am. J. Physiol.*, **62**, 162 (1922).

(8) BANTING, F. G, BEST, C. H., COLLIP, J. B, MACLEOD, J. J. R., NOBLE, E. C., AND HEPBURN, J.: Preliminary studies on the physiological effects of insulin. *Trans. Roy. Soc. Canada*, **16**, 1 (1922).

(9) BANTING, F. G., BEST, C. H., AND NOBLE, C.: Pancreatic extracts in the treatment of diabetes mellitus. *Bull. Battle Creek Sanitarium,* Jan., 1923.

(10) BEST, C. H., AND SCOTT, D. A.: Insulin in tissues other than the pancreas. *J. Am. Med. Assoc.,* **81,** 382 (1923).

(11) BISCHOFF, F.: Preparation of some substituted guanidines. *J. Biol. Chem.,* **80,** 345 (1928).

(12) BISCHOFF, F., BLATHERWICK, N. R. AND SAHYUN, M.: Concerning the similarity of glukhorment and synthalin. *J. Biol. Chem.,* **77,** 467 (1928).

(13) BISCHOFF, F., AND SAHYUN, M.: Denaturation of insulin protein by concentrated sulfuric acid. *J. Biol. Chem.,* **81,** 167 (1929).

(14) BISCHOFF, F., SAHYUN, M., AND LONG, M. L.: Guanidine structure and hypoglycemia. *J. Biol. Chem.,* **81,** 325 (1929).

(15) BLATHERWICK, N. R., BISCHOFF, F., MAXWELL, L. C., BERGER, J., AND SAHYUN, M.: Studies on insulin. *J. Biol. Chem.,* **72,** 57 (1927).

(16) BLATHERWICK, N. R., SAHYUN, M., AND HILL, E.: Some effects of synthalin on metabolism. *J. Biol. Chem.,* **75,** 671 (1927).

(17) BRUGSCH, H., AND HORSTERS, H.: Insulin im Harn. *Arch. f. Exp. Path. u. Pharmak.,* **148,** 309 (1930).

(18) CARR, F. H., CULHANE, K., FULLER, A. T., AND UNDERHILL, S. W. F., A reversible inactivation of insulin. *Biochem. J.,* **23,** 1010 (1929).

(19) COLLIP, J. B.: Glucokinin. *Trans. Roy. Soc. Canada,* **17,** 39 (1923).

(20) COLLIP, J. B.: Glucokinin. A new hormone present in plant tissue. *J. Biol. Chem.,* **56,** 513 (1923).

(21) COLLIP, J. B.: Glucokinin. *J. Biol. Chem.,* **57,** 65 (1923).

(22) COLLIP, J. B.: Some recent advances in endocrinology. *Canadian Med. Assoc. J.,* Sept., 1924.

(23) CORI, C. F.: The influence of insulin and epinephrine on the fate of sugar in the animal body. *Harvey Lectures,* 1927–1928. (Williams & Wilkins, Baltimore. 1929.)

(24) DINGEMAUSE, E.: Über die Reinigung des Insulins. *Arch. f. Exp. Path. u. Pharmak.,* **128,** 44 (1928).

(25) DIRSCHERL, W.: Die Wirkung von Pepsin auf Insulin und seine Acetylderivate. *Zt. physiol. Chem.,* **180,** 217 (1929).

(26) DIRSCHERL, W.: Untersuchungen der Einheitlichkeit von Insulin-praparaten. *Zt. physiol. Chem.,* **202,** 116 (1931).

(27) DODDS, E. C., AND DICKENS, F.: A simple method for the preparation of insulin by aqueous extraction. *Lancet,* I, 330 (1924).

(28) DODDS, E. C., AND DICKENS, F.: Some observations on the properties and preparation of insulin, with special reference to the picrate-acetone method of preparation. *Brit. J. Exp. Path.,* **5,** 115 (1924).

(29) DOISY, E. A., SOMOGYI, M., AND SHAFFER, P. A.: Some properties of an active constituent of pancreas (insulin). *J. Biol. Chem.,* **55,** 31 (1923).

(30) DROLET, G. J.: Diabetes mortality in New York City during the thirty-year period 1901–1931. *J. Am. Med. Assoc.*, **100**, 733 (1933).

(31) DUDLEY, H. W.: The purification of insulin and some of its properties. *Biochem. J.*, **17**, 376 (1923).

(32) DUDLEY, H. W.: Insulin from the cod fish. The direct application of picric acid to the islet tissue. *Biochem. J.*, **18**, 665 (1924).

(33) DUNCAN, G. G.: Synthalin in treatment of diabetes mellitus. *Am. J. Med. Sci.*, **175**, 196 (1928).

(34) FAIRCHILD, B. T.: The pancreas gland. *Ind. and Eng. Chem.*, **16**, 41 (1924).

(35) FOSTER, N. B.: Insulin: its use and misuse. *J. Am. Med. Assoc.*, **94**, 1972 (1930).

(36) FRANK, E., NOTHMANN, M., AND WAGNER, A.: Über synthetisch dargestellte Körper mit insulinartige wirkung auf den Normalen und Diabetischen Organismus. *Klin. Woch.*, **5**, 2100 (1926).

(37) FREUDENBERG, K., AND DIRSCHERL, W.: Die Acetylierung des Insulins. *Zt. physiol. Chem.*, **175**, 1 (1928).

(38) FREUDENBERG, K., AND DIRSCHERL, W.: Insulin. 10. Mitteilung. *Zt. physiol. Chem.*, **202**, 192 (1931).

(39) FREUDENBERG, K., DIRSCHERL, W., EICHEL, H., AND WEISS, E.: Die Einwirkung proteolytischer Fermente auf Insulin. *Zt. physiol. Chem.*, **202**, 159 (1931).

(40) FREUDENBERG, K., DIRSCHERL, W., AND EYER, H.: Beiträge zur Chemie des Insulins. *Zt. physiol. Chem.*, **187**, 89 (1930).

(41) FREUDENBERG, K., DIRSCHERL, W., AND EYER, H.: Beiträge zur Chemie des Insulins. 8. Mitteilung. *Zt. physiol. Chem.*, **202**, 128 (1931).

(42) FREUDENBERG, K., WEISS, E., AND EICHEL, H.: Beiträge zur Chemie des Insulins. 11. Die Wirkung proteolytischer Fermente auf Insulin und seine Derivate. *Zt. physiol. Chem.*, **213**, 226 (1932).

(43) FUNK, C.: Isolation of insulin. *Science*, **63**, 401 (1926).

(44) FUNK, C.: The dissolution of insulin into two new active substances. *Science*, **65**, 39 (1927).

(45) GERLOUGH, T. D., AND BATES, R. W.: The purification and some properties of insulin. *J. Pharmacol.*, **45**, 19 (1932).

(46) HARINGTON, C. R., AND SCOTT, D. A.: Observations on insulin. Part 1. Chemical observations. *Biochem. J.*, **23**, 384 (1929).

(47) HUTCHINSON, H. B., SMITH, W., AND WINTER, L. B.: Studies in carbohydrate metabolism. II. On the preparation of an anti-diabetic hormone from yeast. *Biochem. J.*, **17**, 683 (1923).

(48) JENSEN, H.: The chemical study of insulin. *Science*, **75**, 614 (1932).

(49) JENSEN, H., AND EVANS, Jr., E. A.: Die Einwirkung von Saure und Alkali auf Insulin. *Zt. physiol. Chem.*, **209**, 134 (1932).

(49a) JENSEN, H., AND EVANS, JR., E. A.: The chemistry of insulin. *Physiol. Rev.*, 1934 (in press).

(50) JENSEN, H., AND GEILING, E. M. K.: Studies on crystalline insulin. VII. The acetylation of crystalline insulin, and the behaviour of insulin towards alkali. *J. Pharmacol.*, **33**, 511 (1928).

(51) JENSEN, H., AND LAWDER, A. DE: Studies on crystalline insulin. IX. The adsorption of insulin on charcoal. *J. Biol. Chem.*, **87**, 701 (1930).

(52) JENSEN, H., AND LAWDER, A. DE: Ueber die Aktivierung von Insulin. Untersachungen an kristallisiertem Insulin. *Biochem. Zt.*, **225**, 141 (1930).

(53) JENSEN, H., AND WINTERSTEINER, O.: Studies on crystalline insulin. XIV. The isolation of glutamic acid. *J. Biol. Chem.*, **97**, 93 (1932).

(54) JENSEN, H., AND WINTERSTEINER, O.: Studies on crystalline insulin. XVII. The hydrolysis products of insulin. *J. Biol. Chem.*, **98**, 281 (1932).

(55) JENSEN, H., WINTERSTEINER, O., AND GEILING, E. K.: Studies on crystalline insulin. VIII. The isolation of crystalline insulin from fish islets (cod and pollock) and from the pig's pancreas. The activity of crystalline insulin and further remarks on its preparation. *J. Pharmacol.*, **36**, 115 (1929).

(56) JENSEN, H., WINTERSTEINER, O., AND VIGNEAUD, V. DU: Studies on crystalline insulin. IV. The isolation of arginine, histidine and leucine. *J. Pharmacol.*, **32**, 387 (1928).

(57) JOSLIN, E. P.: The treatment of diabetes mellitus. (Lea & Febiger, Philadelphia, 1928.)

(58) JOSLIN, E. P.: An appraisal of the present treatment of diabetes. *J. Am. Med. Assoc.*, **97**, 595 (1931).

(59) KAHN, M.: Odd carbon fats in the treatment of diabetes ketosis. *Am J. Med. Sci.*, **166**, 826 (1923).

(60) KUHN, W., EYER, H., AND FREUDENBERG, K.: Das optische Verhalten des Insulins und Seiner Derivate. *Zt. physiol. Chem.*, **202**, 97 (1931).

(61) LEWIS, H. B., AND IZUME, S.: The influence of hydrazine and its derivatives on metabolism. *J. Biol. Chem.*, **71**, 33, 51 (1926).

(62) MACLEOD, J. J. R.: Insulin. XIth International Physiological Congress, Edinburgh, 1923.

(63) MACLEOD, J. J. R.: The status of insulin. *J. Am. Med. Assoc.*, **80**, 1238 (1923).

(64) MACLEOD, J. J. R.: Insulin: its action, its therapeutic value in diabetes and its manufacture. *J. Am. Med. Assoc.*, **80**, 1847 (1923).

(65) MACLEOD, J. J. R.: Insulin. *Physiol. Rev.*, **4**, 21 (1924).

(66) MACLEOD, J. J. R.: Carbohydrate metabolism and insulin. (Longmans, Green & Co., New York. 1926.)

(67) MUNCH, J. C.: Bioassays. (Williams & Wilkins, Baltimore. 1931.)

(68) MURLIN, J. R.: Progress in the preparation of pancreatic extracts for the treatment of diabetes. *Endocrinology*, **7**, 519 (1923).

(69) New and Non-official Remedies, 1933 (Amer. Med. Assoc., Chicago).

(70) RINGER, A. I.: Synthalin: use and treatment of diabetes. *Arch. Int. Med.*, **41**, 453 (1928).

(71) SCOTT, D. A.: The action of trypsin on insulin. *J. Biol. Chem.*, **63**, 641 (1925).

(72) SCOTT, D. A.: A further investigation of the chemical properties of insulin. *J. Biol. Chem.*, **65**, 601 (1925).

(73) SCOTT, D. A., AND FISHER, A. M.: An attempt at peptic synthesis of insulin. *J. Gen. Physiol.*, **16**, 741 (1933).

(74) SHONLE, H. A.: The preparation and chemistry of insulin. *J. Chem. Educ.*, **3**, 134 (1926).

(75) SHONLE, H. A., AND WALDO, J. H.: Some chemical reactions of the substance containing insulin. *J. Biol. Chem.*, **58**, 731 (1924).

(76) SJOGREN, B., AND SVEDBERG, T.: The molecular weight of insulin. *J. Am. Chem. Soc.*, **53**, 2657 (1931).

(77) SOMOGYI, M., DOISY, E. A., AND SHAFFER, P. A.: On the preparation of insulin. *J. Biol. Chem.*, **60**, 31 (1924).

(78) STAMMERS, A. D.: A review of recent advances in the study of blood sugar and diabetes. *Physiol. Rev.*, **6**, 630 (1926).

(79) VIGNEAUD, V. DU: The sulfur of insulin. *J. Biol. Chem.*, **75**, 393 (1927).

(80) VIGNEAUD, V. DU, GEILING, E. M. K., AND EDDY, C. A.: Studies on crystalline insulin. VI. Further contributions to the question whether or not crystalline insulin is an adsorption product. *J. Pharmacol.*, **33**, 497 (1928).

(81) VIGNEAUD, V. DU, JENSEN, H., AND WINTERSTEINER, O.: Studies on crystalline insulin. III. Further observations on the crystallization of insulin and on the nature of the sulfur linkage. The isolation of cystine and tyrosine from hydrolyzed crystalline insulin. *J. Pharmacol.*, **32**, 367 (1928)

(82) WATSON, E. M., AND DICK, W. S.: Some observations concerning a possible insulin-inhibiting substance in urine. *Annals Int. Med.*, **6**, 1171 (1933).

(83) WIDMARK, E. M. P.: Observations on the solubility of insulin. *Biochem. J.*, **17**, 668 (1923).

Chapter IV

THE PITUITARY HORMONES

For an introduction to the general subject of the pituitary we can do no better than refer the reader to the articles by Abel (1), Geiling (45) and Cushing (18a). An enormous amount of work has been done on this gland, particularly in connection with the function of the anterior pituitary. While much of importance has been accomplished, there is much that is confusing and unsatisfactory. The number of alleged hormones present in the pituitary is legion and their number is augmented daily. The chemical work is also far from satisfactory. None of the pituitary hormones has so far been isolated in the chemically pure state. Here, however, the excuse may well be offered that all the evidence points to a complex chemical make-up for these substances; far more complex, for example, than for the male and female hormones. This difficulty, added to the relative instability of pituitary hormones, makes progress in their chemistry slow indeed.

However, little difficulty has been encountered in preparing active fractions.

THE ANTERIOR LOBE

The secretions of the anterior pituitary are alleged to be responsible for the following phenomena (4): induction of ovulation; stimulation of ovary to secretion of estrogenic substance; production of luteinization in follicles either with or without ovulation (luteinization may also be induced by direct intrafollicular injection of urine of pregnancy), leading to the secretion of *progestin* (see p. 183); induction of uterine bleeding with combined action of estrogenic substance; production of mammary proliferation and lactation; production of marked hypertrophy of seminal vesicles and prostate; growth; thyroid-stimulation; and regulation of fat metabolism. (See also, (97).)

We shall take these up in turn.

The sex-stimulating hormone of the anterior pituitary

For convincing proof of the intimate relationship existing between the pituitary and the gonads we thank Smith and Engle (82) and Zondek and Aschheim (102).[1] The latter also made the important practical discovery that an anterior pituitary-like hormone is discharged in the urine of pregnant women (7). Smith and Engle made transplantations of anterior pituitary tissue from mice, rats, cats, rabbits and guinea pigs into sexually immature mice and rats of both sexes. These transplantations rapidly induced precocious sexual maturity in the female as evidenced by the appearance of all the changes characteristic of sexual maturity in untreated animals maturing within the usual time, and also as shown by mating. (The genital system of the immature male did not respond so rapidly to the transplantations as did the female.) "The results secured by anterior-pituitary transplantations in the normal animal are harmonious with those secured from hypophysectomy and a replacement therapy. After hypophysectomy, the gonads degenerate. The large follicles become atretic. Pituitary transplants restore the gonads to a normal or nearly normal size, causing a resumption of follicular growth and a reappearance of oestrus in the female, and induce spermatogenesis in the male." Obviously, we are here dealing with hormonic control.

Zondek (103), in developing methods of extraction, also developed a standard test method. His mouse unit he defined as the minimum quantity which, when divided into six portions and injected in the course of two days, will mature the ovaries of an infantile mouse (weighing not over

[1] See also (65).

6 grams) in 100 hours subsequent to the first injection.
Zondek discovered that extracts from pregnant urine gave
this test; and then he elaborated methods of concentrating
the material (106) (63). The hormone, he found, could be
precipitated with alcohol and was soluble in water. The
female hormone, present in the urine, could be removed by
ether extraction—a solvent in which the anterior pituitary
hormone was insoluble. In one of his experiments, Zondek
slightly acidified the urine with acetic acid and evaporated
in vacuo to half its volume at 40°C. (The hormone, he
found, was destroyed at higher temperatures.) The material was filtered, the theelin removed from the filtrate by
repeated extraction with ether, the ether-insoluble portion
dialyzed and finally evaporated to dryness *in vacuo* at 40°C.
The product was again treated with ether, to remove traces
of theelin, and the residue was dissolved in water.[2]

Sex-stimulating hormones can be obtained from anterior
pituitaries, from the placenta (p. 187), from the blood of
pregnant animals (p. 80) and, as has already been said,
from the urine of pregnant animals (which, by the way, is
by far the most convenient source). It should, however,
be pointed out even at this stage that there are differences
of opinion as to the identity of the hormones obtained from
the pituitary with those obtained from the urine of the pregnant animal (see p. 97). The hormones, all the evidence
shows, are quite different.[3] In fact, the weight of evidence

----

[2] In carrying out the pregnancy test, Zondek (7) injects from 0.2 to
0.4 cc. of urine from the pregnant animal into immature female mice twice
daily for three days. The mice are killed on the fifth day (100 hours after
the first injection) and the ovaries are examined. The hormone is identified by noticing corpora lutea and follicles filled with blood (for details,
see (63)).

[3] "It is possible by the use of the active material from pituitary glands
to grow enormous ovaries in immature rats. On the other hand, the amount
of growth which can be produced by placental extracts and by preparations
from pregnancy urine seems to be limited" (36). Zondek, who has given
the name *prolan* to the hormone under discussion, gives the name *prolan A*

tends to support the theory that the anterior pituitary-like hormone from pregnancy urine is derived from the placenta (15a, 64a).

Methods of preparing the anterior pituitary (sex) hormone

Evans (34) is largely responsible for the belief that acid extracts of the pituitary contain the sex hormones, whereas the alkaline extracts contain the growth hormone. The separation is certainly not a sharp one, for alkaline extracts have been shown to contain very abundant sex-stimulating hormone. In fact, Bugbee (12) uses an alkaline extract for his preparation. Fresh sheep pituitaries are frozen at the packing house and shipped in that condition. The glands are spread out and allowed to thaw at room temperature and ground very fine. Four hundred cubic centimeters of 0.05 N sodium hydroxide and 0.4 per cent "tricresol" are added for every 100 grams of pituitary powder.[4] The mixture is stirred at intervals during an hour. The extract is then neutralized to pH 7.2 to 7.6 (salmon pink to phenol red) with N sulfuric acid. The extract is centrifuged, and the supernatant liquid may be used for injections.

A second and a third extract of the residue with sodium hydroxide will produce more of the active material.

The extracts are effective in doses of 1 cc. daily for 3 days when injected subcutaneously into immature rats. When

to the follicle-stimulating hormone and *prolan B* to the luteinizing hormone. The former he extracted from the urine of women in the menopause and after ovariectomy. The extract injected into mice produces only stimulation of follicles with ripening and ovulation. Prolan B, which he prepared from the anterior prituitary, produces luteinization of follicle walls (97) (98) (99) (100) (20) (25).

Zondek uses the term *prolan* for the gonadotropic principle of the anterior lobe and for the active material found in the urine of pregnancy. Prolan is a patented trade name for the product made by the *I. G. Farben Industrie* (25).

[4] The authors found that active extracts could be obtained by using the entire gland from the sheep.

given for 6 or 9 days they cause hypertrophy of the ovaries to 5 to 10 times the size of ovaries of controls of the same age.

The sex hormone is not injured by 0.4 per cent "tricresol", whereas the growth hormone is completely destroyed. The sex hormone can be salted out with 20 per cent sodium sulfate. It is relatively stable in weak alkali but rapidly destroyed by acids. It is destroyed by slightly elevated temperatures.

In somewhat marked contrast to the work of Bugbee is that of Fevold and Hisaw (38) who find that the gonad-stimulating hormone is readily destroyed by $N/100$ NaOH. They have introduced a method of extraction which has been widely copied. They use aqueous pyridine as their solvent. They find that it is possible to prepare two active fractions from their aqueous pyridine extract: one is water-soluble and produces primarily follicular development in the ovaries of sexually immature rats, and the other, which is relatively insoluble in water, produces no follicular effect upon the ovaries. However, when the two fractions are united a typical luteinized ovary results; which indicates that the water-insoluble fraction is potent for luteinization when the follicles have been stimulated by the follicular stimulating hormone (54).[5]

Fevold's method of preparation is as follows (38): Five grams of dried anterior lobe are extracted for twelve hours with 200 cc. of 50 per cent aqueous pyridine. The extraction is carried out at room temperature in a test tube fitted with a continuous stirrer. The extract is next removed by centrifuging and the insoluble material is again extracted with aqueous pyridine. The two extracts are united and evaporated to dryness at 35°C. The residue may be emulsified in water and injected subcutaneously. This extract produces

[5] There is some opposition to this point of view. Evans (34) is (or was?) of the opinion that the luteinizing hormone is identical with the growth hormone.

sexual maturity in immature female rats, great follicular growth in the ovary, together with numerous corpora lutea.

For all ordinary purposes, the method just outlined yields a potent extract, and, as has already been indicated, has been widely used with uniformly excellent results. If, however, the separation of the two hormones be desired, the method is as follows: the dried pyridine extract is thoroughly triturated with distilled water and the insoluble material is removed by centrifuging. The residue is re-extracted and again centrifuged. The water solution is evaporated to dryness in an air-dryer and again taken up in water, centrifuging off all insoluble material. The procedure is repeated until the product is readily soluble in distilled water. The gonad-stimulating hormone is taken up in the water, while most of the luteinizing hormone remains in the water-insoluble fraction.

The aqueous solution may be further purified by adding five volumes of 99 per cent alcohol when the active material is precipitated. The precipitate is centrifuged off, freed from alcohol and dissolved in distilled water. The aqueous solution is adjusted to pH 4.0 to 5.0 and allowed to stand for 8 to 10 hours. The precipitate which forms is centrifuged off. The aqueous solution is neutralized to pH 6.8 to 7, precipitated with four volumes of alcohol and dissolved in water. It may be preserved by the addition of one volume of alcohol.

This extract injected into immature female rats brings about sexual maturity in three days, with production of large follicles in the ovaries, and with no (or only slight) indications of luteinization.

The water-insoluble residue, which contains the luteinizing hormone, is washed with distilled water and taken up in $N/200$ sodium hydroxide. The solution is allowed to stand for 8 to 10 hours, with occasional shaking, centrifuged, and the insoluble material is discarded. The solution is neutralized and five volumes of alcohol are added. After the precipitate has separated out it is centrifuged, freed from alcohol and taken up in water at pH 7.6 to 7.8.

This preparation does not have the ability to bring an animal to sexual maturity, but it does luteinize the follicles produced by the gonad-stimulating fraction. If this fraction is united to the gonad-stimulating preparation, the two together produce the large luteinized ovary similar to that obtained by the use of the whole pyridine extract.

Fevold and Hisaw (38) give explicit details for methods of testing their products. They are of the opinion that the follicle-stimulating hormone obtained from the pituitary is identical with Zondek's prolan A (p. 72) obtained from urine. They also believe that Collip's *emmenin*, obtained from human placentae (p. 187), which has a stimulating action on the immature ovary, is different from the anterior lobe hormones in that the latter are insoluble in acetone and 99 per cent alcohol, whereas *emmenin* is soluble in these solvents. The placental hormone, further, is relatively insoluble in water, whereas the gonad-stimulating hormone of the anterior lobe is readily soluble. A fraction obtained by Collip, insoluble in 85 per cent alcohol (p. 187), which also has a stimulating effect on the ovary, resembles more closely the anterior pituitary hormones.

In a recent paper (37), Fevold outlines further improvements in the preparation of extracts.

For the preparation of the non-fractionated extract, desiccated anterior lobe powder (obtained from one of the pharmaceutical houses) is extracted with 50 per cent aqueous pyridine, as described above. The extract is evaporated, the residue emulsified in water (50 cc. per 5 grams of dried sheep powder) and one-half volume acetone added. The precipitate is centrifuged off, reprecipitated and discarded. The solution is concentrated at 40°C. to an aqueous sludge and 4 to 5 volumes of acetone are added. The precipitate is separated by centrifuging, taken up in water (10 cc. per 5 grams of powder) and two volumes of acetone are added. The precipitate is again centrifuged off and the supernatant liquid (which is inactive) is discarded. The precipitate is taken up in water (10 cc. per 5 grams of original pituitary powder) and centrifuged. To the solution is added 5 cc. of acetone, and the precipitate which separates out is removed by centrifuging, reemulsified in water and reprecipitated from 33 per cent acetone. The 33 per cent acetone solutions (which contain the active material) are united and 3 to 4 volumes of acetone are added. This precipitates the active material. It is removed by centrifuging, taken up in 10 cc. water, and the purification by means of 33 per cent acetone is repeated as before. The final 33 per cent acetone-soluble product is taken up in water or normal saline solution.

The extract when concentrated so that 1 cc. contains 40 to 50 rat units is light brown in color. (The rat unit is defined as that amount of active material which will produce sexual maturity in immature female rats, 21 days old at the beginning of the experiment, with a corresponding increase in the weight of the ovaries of 50 to 100 per cent.) The material is injected subcutaneously, twice daily, over a period of 5 days. Rabbits have also been used.

Further purification of the follicular-stimulating hormone is also described. At 50 per cent concentration of alcohol and water, the follicular-stimulating substance is quite soluble, while the luteinizing factor is partially precipitated. If the percentage of alcohol is raised to 60 per cent, the luteinizing substance is completely precipitated, together with some of the follicular-stimulating hormone. The soluble fraction produces large ovaries with little or no lutein growth.

Fevold and Hisaw find that benzoic acid precipitates material rich in luteinizing power but poor in follicular-stimulating action; which is somewhat at variance with the work of Katzman and Doisy (p. 98).

It must be emphasized that there is at present no unanimity of opinion with regard to the view held by Zondek, Fevold and Hisaw and several others that what is commonly called the anterior pituitary sex-stimulating hormone really consists of two hormones. Fevold and Hisaw discuss this question in their latest paper (37). Van Dyke (90) states that he could not confirm their work.

Van Dyke (90), who suggests the name *hebin* ("puberty") for the gonad-stimulating principle, prepares his material as follows: The *entire* sheep gland is dried with acetone. The last traces of acetone are removed *in vacuo*, and the material is powdered. To X grams powder (A) XO cc. $M/7.5$ sodium acetate-acetic acid buffer, pH 4.5, is added, and the mixture is kept in the ice-box overnight. The material is next centrifuged, and the residue is again extracted. The combined extracts have a pH of 4.8. Alcohol is now added to the extracts until the concentration is 90 per cent. A precipitate forms. The filtrate, which is inactive, is removed by decantation. The precipitate is collected by centrifuging; it is washed twice with alcohol and finally with ether. The precipitate is dried *in vacuo* at room temperature and powdered (B). This material is used for injections. The yield of (B) is 4.7 to 5 per cent of the weight of the original powder (A).

Hebin, Van Dyke finds, is not dialyzable. It can be heated *for a short time* without any harm. Van Dyke states in this paper that alkaline extracts are also good source material.

In a later paper (91), Van Dyke takes issue with Fevold and Hisaw, who claim to have separated the active material into two hormones, one being follicular-stimulating, and the other being responsible for luteinization.

The details of Van Dyke's modified process are as follows: The whole pituitaries of sheep are dehydrated with acetone and powdered, as before. To X gram powder are added 20X cc. of freshly-standardized 0.02 N ammonium hydroxide. This is shaken occasionally and allowed to stand at room temperature for 24 hours. The pH of the mixture falls to 9 to 10. Without separating the undissolved solids, the pH is lowered to 5 to 5.6 with glacial acetic acid. The material is next centrifuged and the supernatant fluid removed. The residue is washed with acetate buffer (pH 5 to 5.6). The combined volume of fluid and washings (which contain the gonad-stimulating hormone) amounts to 20X cc. Alcohol is now added until the percentage reaches 35 by volume. The precipitate is allowed to settle, the supernatant fluid is decanted, and the precipitate, which is inactive, is washed with 35 per cent alcohol. Alcohol is now added to the combined filtrates until the percentage reaches 70 by volume. The precipitate is allowed to stand in the ice-box overnight, and it is then washed with absolute alcohol and ether.

The precipitate represents 2.7 per cent by weight of the original material. It remains active for five months if kept at 4°C., in aqueous solution, and at pH 3.7 to 6.4. Alkaline solutions (pH 7.5) are stable for 2 months, at least. The purified preparation in aqueous solution (pH 4.9 to 5.4) is destroyed by boiling. Filtering an aqueous solution of the hormone (at alkaline or acid pH) through a Berkefeld filter does not remove the hormone.

Properties of the anterior pituitary hormones[6]

The active material from whatever source is insoluble in organic solvents and is precipitated from aqueous solution by such solvents as alcohol or acetone (36). The hormone (or hormones) does not dialyze and is destroyed by strong acids and alkalis. It is also destroyed by heat. It is soluble not only in water but in acetic, sulfosalicylic and tartaric

---

[6] It is rather difficult at this stage to make sharp distinctions in properties between the true anterior pituitary hormone and the anterior pituitary-like hormone from the urine.

acids (60).   According to Fischer (39), his most active preparations give positive biuret, Millon, Pauli and Molisch
reactions, but the Hopkins-Cole is negative.   The hormone
is precipitated by saturated ammonium sulfate, uranyl acetate, phosphotungstic acid, phosphomolybdic acid and
tannic acid, especially in acidified solution.   Picric acid,
ammonium molybdate, copper acetate and silver nitrate
fail to give precipitates.

Fischer, starting with a commercial preparation, prepared
his active fraction by a series of steps involving (a) precipitation of phosphate with barium acetate; (b) precipitation
of the hormone in the filtrate with alcohol; (c) the addition
of $Ba(OH)_2$ to the concentrated solution of the hormone and
precipitation of the excess barium by CO_2 concentration of
the filtrate and precipitation of the hormone with alcohol.
Further purification was accomplished by long-continued
dialysis and precipitation of the solutions with mixtures of
alcohol and ether.   Haurowitz (72) claims that trypsin destroys his active material, but the polypeptidases do not;
suggesting a substance of high molecular weight.   (See, also,
(105).)

Anterior pituitary-like sex hormone in the blood

Zondek very early in his work showed the presence of this
hormone in the blood of pregnant women.   The hormone
in the blood of pregnant mares seems to be much nearer the
true anterior pituitary hormone than the one found in the
blood of the pregnant woman.   In this country Frank has
done a great deal of work in this field.   For a general discussion, see (63, p. 175).

Hormone of the intermediary lobe of the hypophysis

Within the last year Zondek (104) has published an account of the isolation of a specific hormone derived from the
intermediary lobe of the hypophysis, to which the name

intermedin has been given.   This hormone can be obtained by
extracting the acetone-extracted dried powdered hypophysis
with 0.25 per cent acetic acid.   As a test object, the minnow
(*Phoxinus laevis*), a small fish, is used, which at the spawning
time develops the "nuptual dress."   Intermedin does what
theelin or prolan fail to do: when intermedin is injected into
the fish at a time other than the spawning period, the minnows
develop an intensive red coloration at the sights of attachment
of the pectoral, ventral and anal fins.   (This red coloration
is present during the spawning period.)

The anterior pituitary: physiological discussions and possible
clinical applications

Consult the following references, among others: (67) (25)
(13) (14) (9) (77) (85) (63).

The growth hormone of the anterior pituitary

We owe to Evans the concrete evidence for the existence
of this growth-controlling factor.   Biologically, the evidence
is convincing, but chemically, much remains to be done.
The difficulties in this field, as Evans (33a) has pointed out
are several: the hormone is apparently a substance complex
enough to resemble the proteins; it is very labile; "its effects
can be detected only when it is administered frequently, par-
enterally, and over a sufficiently long time interval, with adequate controls, to an adequately standardized animal."

In his earliest experiments, beginning with 1921, Evans
(31), (27) used saline suspensions of beef anterior pituitaries
for intraperitoneal injection into rats.   These injections
were repeated daily for several weeks, with the result that
some of the experimental rats grew to twice the size of the
untreated controls.   An active alkaline extract was subsequently prepared as follows (34) (30): To 2000 grams of
beef anterior hypophysis (which may be stored for 18 to
24 months with solid CO_2, after having been ground) are

added 12,000 cc. distilled water and 3000 cc. O.2 N barium hydroxide, then thoroughly mixed and centrifuged and filtered. Two-tenths N sulfuric acid is next added to the filtrate until the pH of the mixture is about 8. The barium not already precipitated by sulfuric acid is removed by a slight excess of sodium sulfate. The mixture is again centrifuged, and filtered. This extract (15 liters) is kept frozen until needed for injection (the temperature of the extract is never allowed to rise above 10°C. during the course of its preparation.) Injected into normal adult female rats weighing 250 to 270 grams, the extract created an increase in body weight of about 35 grams in 20 days when administered in a daily intraperitoneal dose of 0.125 cc. and a growth of 55 grams when given in 1 cc. doses. Male rats are more variable than females in their response to the growth hormone (35).

Evans (35) gives a modified procedure in a subsequent paper. X grams of fresh bovine anterior lobes are ground in a mortar with 2 X grams clean sand. The mixture is weighed and 2 cc. of water are added for every 1 gram of ground gland. The volume of the mixture is now measured and three-eighths of a volume of 0.2 N sodium hydroxide is added. The material is kept in the ice-box for 12 hours. The alkaline extract is neutralized with 0.2 N acetic acid. Enough acid is added so that the reaction of phenol red is yellow (acid side). Alkali is next added until the phenol red indicator shows the first pink stage.

Not only does the hormone produce experimental gigantism in rats but it provokes the growth of hypophysectomized puppies (204).

It is in one of his early papers (34) that Evans makes the statement that alkaline aqueous extracts are maximally effective in stimulating growth in adults at levels which never provoke maturity in young animals; whereas acid aqueous extracts are effective in provoking maturity in young animals at levels which do not stimulate growth in adults. He finds that the growth hormone, unlike the sex-stimulating hormone, is absent in the urine of pregnant women. He further records that the sex-stimulating hormone passes the Berkefeld filter in acid solution, whereas the growth hormone fails to do so; the sex-stimulating hormone cannot be adsorbed by kaolin in acid solution, whereas the growth hormone is adsorbed. The growth hormone can be precipitated from its alkaline solution by means of acetone, and the active powder so obtained is stable at room temperature if kept in a vacuum desiccator. Of course, this material still contains a very large quantity of gonad-stimulating hormone. Both hormones are completely precipitated by phosphotungstic acid and by flaviaric acid. Trichloracetic acid completely precipitates the growth hormone, but not the gonad-stimulating hormone. The latter, practically free of gonad-stimulating hormone, can be obtained from the supernatant trichloracetic acid solution by precipitation with phosphotungstic acid or flavianic acid. Acetic acid, in concentrations of 95 to 98 per cent, will dissolve the growth-stimulating hormone without destroying it, whereas much of the gonad-stimulating hormone is destroyed. The precipitation of the active acid extracts with acetone (in the presence of quinine sulfate) give active growth-promoting powders practically devoid of gonad-stimulating properties (33a).

An improvement in the method of preparing the active extract was accomplished by Teel (68) (86), who used sodium sulfate for fractionating purposes. The neutralized alkaline extract is prepared as described above. The solution is warmed to 35°C. and 20 grams of anhydrous sodium sulfate for each 100 cc. of extract is added slowly and with stirring. At the end of 15 minutes the precipitate is filtered, pressed and taken up in one-half the original volume of water. (There is sufficient sodium sulfate in the precipitate to redissolve

this water-insoluble fraction.) The redissolved precipitate
is filtered through a sterilized Seitz filter and is then ready
for injection.

The protein precipitate, consisting of several globulins, has
been further fractionated with sodium sulfate. The fraction
from 20 to 35 per cent sodium sulfate, which brings down a
large amount of protein, is devoid of growth-promoting
properties.

In conjunction with Cushing, Teel injected his active
material for over a year in an English bulldog, and a condition closely simulating human acromegaly developed (87).

Bugbee, basing his work on Teel, developed the following
method of preparation (12): Beef pituitaries are frozen at
the packing house, the anterior lobes are separated and
ground very fine. To every 100 grams of anterior lobes is
added 400 cc. of 0.05 N sodium hydroxide. The mixture
is stirred at intervals and then allowed to stand in the refrigerator overnight. It is neutralized to pH 7.2 to 7.6 with 0.2 N
acetic acid. The mixture is centrifuged for $\frac{1}{2}$ hour, the
cloudy supernatant liquid is heated to 37°C. and to every
100 cc. is added 20 grams of sodium sulfate. The mixture
is centrifuged for $\frac{1}{2}$ hour, and the protein precipitate is
dissolved as far as possible in 0.02 N sodium hydroxide so
that 2 cc. represent the extractives of 1 gram of anterior lobe.
The gland residue, left after centrifugation of the first extract,
is worked up in a similar way with one-half the volume of
0.05 N sodium hydroxide used in the first extract. After
this second extract has been salted out with 20 per cent
sodium sulfate, the precipitate is added to the solution of the
first extract. A sterile product is obtained by filtration
through asbestos and germ-proof porcelain filters. The extract retains its potency for several months if kept in the
refrigerator. Injections of 0.25 to 1 cc. of the extract into
rats over a period of three months caused them to gain in
weight much more than the controls.

Bugbee claims that one essential difference between the sex-stimulating hormone and the growth hormone is that the former is not injured by 0.4 per cent "tricresol" whereas the latter is quickly destroyed. Both hormones can be salted out with 20 per cent sodium sulfate, and both, according to Bugbee, can be kept for many days in weak alkali, although rather quickly destroyed by weak acids.

A very important contribution on the growth hormone appeared in 1930 when Van Dyke (89) published his paper. In this paper, the author emphasizes the importance of using aqueous alkaline solvents. He suggests the name *phyone* ("I cause to grow") for the growth hormone. The anterior lobes are dissected from fresh pituitary beef glands and ground to a fine hash. To X gram anterior lobe, X/2 cc. 1 per cent sodium hydroxide and enough water to make XO cc. are added. (A preservative is carefully avoided.) The mixture is kept at 0°C. for 24 hours, with occasional stirring. The supernatent liquid is decanted through glass wool and the gland residue is well drained with suction. The residue is re-extracted. The pH of the combined extracts is adjusted to 7.2 with hydrochloric acid, the precipitate (inactive) is removed by centrifuging, the cloudy supernatent liquid is warmed to 35°C., and for every 100 cc. of liquid 20 grams of anhydrous sodium sulfate are added, slowly and with stirring.

The material is centrifuged for one hour at high speed. The clean supernatent liquid is quite inactive. The precipitate is washed twice by suspending it in a solution of 20 grams of sodium sulfate in 100 cc. water. The material is centrifuged for one hour. The washed precipitate is suspended in XO 2 cc. water and the pH is adjusted to 7.5. The material is once again centrifuged for one hour. The insoluble residue is discarded. The supernatent fluid is filtered through a Berkefeld filter. The filtrate is refiltered through sterile Berkefeld N. One cubic centimeter of this filtrate corresponds to 0.2 gram of fresh anterior lobe. It represents the crude stock material and may be used for injection into animals.

For clinical application (subcutaneous injection into man), Y cc. of the crude stock is warmed to 35°C. and reprecipitated with 20 grams anhydrous sodium sulfate in 100 cc. of water. The suspension is centrifuged, the supernatent liquid discarded, and the precipitate is washed once by suspending it in 20 grams sodium sulfate dissolved in 100 cc. water. The washed precipitate is suspended in less than Y/4 cc. water and transferred to collodion sacs known to hold back congo red. The material is dialysed for two hours against distilled water. The bulk of the sulfate is thereby removed. A small amount of precipitate which remains is removed by centrifuging and is discarded. The clear supernatent fluid is made alkaline to phenol red.

The pH is next lowered to 4.75 with N acetic acid. The precipitate is centrifuged five minutes. N sodium hydroxide is now added to the supernatent fluid until the pH reaches 7.5 to 8. If the volume is greater than $\frac{1}{4}$ Y, the solution is concentrated by filtration through a 5 per cent gun-cotton membrane, using suction. The alkaline solution is passed through a sterile Berkefeld N and sealed in sterile ampoules. About 0.35 cc. per kilogram of adult or hypophysectomized rat, injected daily for three days, will cause a total weight increase of 3 per cent.

Norite, washed with concentrated hydrochloric acid and washed until chloride-free, adsorbs phyone; but so far no pH will elute the active material.

Van Dyke states that he was unable to isolate phyone from the serum or urine of acromegalic patients. He finds acid extracts of the gland to be inaffective; and he also states that meta-cresol or thymol, added as preservatives, decrease the activity.

For assay, female hypophysectomized rats (80 to 100 g.) are used. Their weight must be practically constant for

24 hours before the injection. The injection is made subcutaneously in amounts proportional to the weight of the
animal. These injections are made daily for three days.
A potent extract will show a significant increase in weight
in 24 hours. (In four days the increase may amount to
16 per cent of the total weight of the animal.)

An increase in weight due to phyone is followed by a
decrease 48 hours after the last injection.

The growth hormone, according to Wadehn (92), can be
precipitated at pH 4.2. The gland is preserved for one to
two weeks with a 1 per cent sodium benzoate. At pH 4.2 the
hormone is precipitated with proteins, but many impurities
are not precipitated at this point. The precipitate is treated
with 1 per cent sodium bicarbonate, which extracts the hormone. For test objects, the authors use the white (male)
mouse, 21 to 25 grams in weight. At the end of 9 days the
mice undergoing the experiment must show an average gain
in weight of 2 grams over the controls.

Using extracts made from the anterior lobe of oxen, and
testing the growth-promoting effects of such extracts upon
totally hypophysectomized rats, Collip has recently succeeded in preparing very potent extracts (16). The anterior lobe tissue is treated with several volumes of dilute
alkali (0.5 to 1 per cent sodium hydroxide or 1 per cent ammonium hydroxide). The mixture is acidified with acetic
acid, filtered, and the residue is again suspended in dilute
alkali, reprecipitated with acetic acid and filtered. This
extraction with dilute acetic acid is repeated 5 times. Ammonia is added to the combined filtrates to give approximately
a 1 per cent concentration. By the addition of appropriate
amounts of calcium chloride and sodium phosphate, a suspension of calcium phosphate is produced in the solution,
and the whole is concentrated at low pressure until the ammonia is removed. The precipitate of calcium phosphate
is filtered, and this precipitate is then extracted repeatedly

with 0.5 per cent sodium hydroxide. The alkaline extracted material is acidified with acetic acid to pH 6.5. It is next made alkaline with ammonia and concentrated at low temperature and pressure to remove the ammonia. The semi-crystalline material which separates out at a pH 7.5 to 8 is removed and extracted with dilute sodium hydroxide. The alkaline solution is almost neutralized and may be used for injections. At this point, 1 cc. represents about 2 grams of original gland material. One-fourth cubic centimeter of this solution administered twice daily to completely hypophysectomized rats has resulted in marked growth.

While the statement has been made in the past that the growth-hormone, unlike the sex-stimulating hormone, is absent from the urine during pregnancy, two German workers claim to have isolated it from the urine of pregnancy (93). The urine is freed from phosphate with magnesia mixture and filtered through glass wool. The hormones in the filtrate are precipitated with ammonium sulfate and redissolved in ammonium hydrogen phosphate. The filtrate is next treated with kaolin, which according to the authors, removes the sex hormones. The growth hormone in the filtrate can be concentrated by adsorption on animal charcoal. The "active charcoal" when implanted subcutaneously into young rats causes accelerated growth. (The authors were apparently not successful in eluting the active material from the charcoal.)

Thyreotropic hormone

Smith and others were able to show that removing the hypophysis in rats gave rise to thyroid atrophy, and that the intramuscular implantation of fresh hypophysis into the hypophysectomized animals developed pronounced reparative changes. In conjunction with Foster, Smith showed that the basal rate of the hypophysectomized animals was invariably lower than that of the normal controls (81) (29). Loeb and his associates (57) showed that when guinea pigs were injected with acid or alkaline extracts of the anterior pituitary gland, the thyroid gland of these animals showed such a remarkable hypertrophy that it closely resembled the thyroid seen in pronounced cases of Graves disease. (See also the paper by Crew and Wiesner (18).)

For the preparation of these extracts, the anterior pituitary of cattle are freed completely from other parts of the hypophysis, then dried and powdered. Five grams of the dried powder are extracted with 100 cc. of 0.5 per cent acetic acid or with 100 cc. of 0.1 per cent sodium hydroxide for a period of 24 hours (in ice chest). The material is filtered, neutralized to pH 7.8 (phenol red), refiltered, and the filtrate is passed through a Seitz bacterial filter to render it sterile (58).

It will be noticed that such impure preparations must contain some of the other pituitary hormones. Whether the action on the thyroid is due to a specific hormone of the anterior pituitary lobe, or whether it represents merely one additional property of a hormone already known, is not altogether clear at present. In any case, these crude acid and alkaline extracts do give rise to hypertrophy of the thyroid gland. Loeb records the daily injection into the guinea pigs of 1 cc. of the extract. On each day, beginning with the second day of the experiment and ending with the seventh, he removed the thyroid gland from one guinea pig of each set. A noticeable hypertrophy was shown even after one injection, both the acid and alkaline extracts behaving pretty much alike. The extracts, as prepared by Loeb, do not cause ovulation or opening of the vagina in the guinea pig.

Acting upon the theory that such extracts of the pituitary gland cause an increased elimination of the thyroid hormone into the circulation, thereby giving rise to an increase in metabolism, Loeb and his associates were able to show that acid extracts of the pituitary glands caused a marked and rapid rise in the basal metabolism of guinea pigs (15). Furthermore, changes in the iodine metabolism (the concentration of alcohol-insoluble or "organic" iodine increasing in the blood and decreasing in the thyroid) were produced in the animal which corresponded to those noted in Graves' disease in man (see, also, (56) (59)).

In the meantime, Schockaert had found that the injection of a saline suspension of fresh anterior pituitary glands induces in young ducks an enlargement of the thyroid gland which in the case of two of them reached 20 and 60 times, respectively, the weight of the controls. Schockaert, in conjunction with Foster (76), showed that after such injections there was a rapid drop in the total iodine content of the thyroid gland. "In man and animals the iodine content of the thyroid is inversely proportional to the degree of hyperplasia . . . the thyroid hypertrophy and hyperplasia induced with anterior pituitary suspensions can be compared, chemically as well as physiologically, with the hyperplasia observed in human hyperthyroidism and exophthalmic goiter." Rather significantly, they found that Van Dyke's growth hormone from the anterior pituitary (which he calls *phyone*) also possesses thyreotropic action. On the other hand, a luteinizing hormone (Squibb) and prolan (the sex-stimulating hormone, presumably of German manufacture) did not influence the percentage of iodine. Greep (46), in Hisaw's laboratory, claims, however, that thyroid hyperplasia can be produced by the luteinizing fraction of the pituitary.

Exophthalmos in the guinea pig has also been produced by Marine (62), using acetic acid extracts of ox anterior pituitary powder. The exophthalmos was obtained with thyroidectomized guinea pigs as well as with animals with intact thyroids.

As if to further complicate the situation, Riddle and his associates (74), working with doves and pigeons, and using a variety of pituitary fractions, come to the conclusion that neither prolactin (see p. 94) nor the growth principle causes the thyroid hypertrophy which follows the injection of certain pituitary extracts. On the other hand, "hyperplasia of the normally developed thyroid following pituitary administration is a specific response to the gonad-stimulating hormone, or to another pituitary derivative having very similar solubilities."

Krogh (53), starting with alkaline extracts of the anterior pituitary, has made a study of some of the chemical properties of the thyreotropic hormone. She finds that it is soluble in water, Ringer's solution and 48 per cent alcohol, but insoluble in 70 per cent alcohol. Much inactive protein material can be removed by precipitation with 70 per cent alcohol and then extraction with water or 48 per cent alcohol.

Collip (3) has recently prepared an active extract of the thyreotropic hormone, though the details of the preparation are not given. The extract, writes Collip, has been obtained from the residues after the removal of the growth hormone. It has been freed of prolactin (p. 94) by isoelectric precipitation of this fraction, and further purified by salt precipitation and fractionation by alcohol and acetone.

Loeser (61) removes his proteins, etc., with trichloracetic acid. The fresh anterior pituitaries are dried with acetone and extracted for 12 hours with 10 volumes of 1.25 per cent ammonium hydroxide. The material is filtered. The extraction with ammonium hydroxide is repeated twice. Trichloracetic acid is added to the combined filtrates until no further precipitate forms. The material is centrifuged, the supernatant liquid is poured off and the residue is extracted with 5 per cent trichloracetic acid. The treatment with the 5 per cent trichloracetic acid is repeated. The precipitate is weakly active. The combined filtrates are added to 10 volumes of acetone, the product is allowed to stand for 12 hours in the ice-box, the supernatant liquid is poured off, and the precipitate is washed twice with acetone. The precipitate is finally dried over phosphorus pentoxide.

The product is readily soluble in water and shows strong thyreotropic properties.   The material can be further purified by first extracting the powder with methyl alcohol, then dissolving the residue in water and precipitating with acetone.[7]

Fat-metabolism hormone in the anterior pituitary gland

In 1931 Anselmino and Hoffmann (5) (48) obtained a fraction from the anterior pituitary which, when injected into rabbits, markedly increased the acetone bodies in the blood. To prepare the active material, the pituitary is dried with acetone, powdered and kept over phosphorus pentoxide (protected from light).   This powder can be kept for a long time without deterioration.

To prepare the extract, the powder is extracted with distilled water for several days at room temperature.   The mixture is then centrifuged, the residue is discarded and the filtrate may be used for animal tests.   If the filtrate is to be employed for injections into humans, the authors suggest the addition of enough sodium chloride to make an isotonic solution, then ultra-filtration through a collodion filter and final sterilization of the solution by Berkefeld filtration.

This *fat-metabolism* hormone is similar in its properties to prolan, the gonad-stimulating hormone; however, the former shows very slight sex-stimulating characteristics.   The fat-metabolism hormone is soluble in water, in 50 per cent alcohol, and insoluble in ether, chloroform and concentrated alcohol.   It is destroyed by heating at 60°C. for fifteen minutes, and it is also destroyed by strong acid and alkali.   It is adsorbed by Kieselgur, but not absorbed by charcoal, kaolin, talcum, asbestos, aluminum hydroxide and ferric hydroxide.

[7] It may be mentioned at this point that Anselmino (6) claims to have shown the presence of an *anti-thyroid* stimulating substance in blood and tissues. The blood is extracted with fat solvents and the product is saponified. The active material is in the fat fraction. When injected, this anti-thyroid substance counterbalances the excessive carbon dioxide production obtained when thyroxine is given.

The fact that prolan is adsorbed by animal charcoal, whereas this fat-metabolism hormone is not, makes a separation of the two possible.

Funk (44) (42) showed that this peculiar fat-metabolism hormone is present in the urine of pregnancy and normal urine. Funk's method is to start with 2 liters of fresh, normal urine and treat it with 60 grams of benzoic acid (dissolved in a minimum quantity of alcohol). The precipitate is filtered, the benzoic acid removed by washing with alcohol, and the small amount of residue which does not dissolve is weighed. The moist residue (between 2.5 to 4.5 grams) is triturated with N ammonium hydroxide (24 cc. for every 3.6 grams of the material).

This crude extract (which is rather toxic) when injected into rats gives rise to 100 mg. of "acetone bodies" in 100 cc. urine two hours after the injection, as compared to 5–6 mg. in the controls. The toxicity can be eliminated by adding acetone (up to 60 per cent) to the ammoniacal extract. "After centrifugation of the large, in most cases inactive, precipitate, the active material is recovered from the supernatant fluid by acidification and addition of more acetone. The precipitate obtained . . . yields when injected 20 to 40 mg. of acetone per 100 cc. urine."

From our own work, it seems as if Funk's fat-metabolism hormone, and an extract recently prepared by Doisy which gives rise to hyperglycemia, are one and the same substance.

Hormone in anterior pituitary involved in carbohydrate metabolism

The fact that in cases of acromegaly glycosuria and diabetes are common, has long suggested a connection between the pituitary and carbohydrate metabolism. Houssay (49) has shown a more specific relationship by pointing out that injection of 0.5 to 1 unit of insulin per kilogram of body weight into a hypophysectomized dog (a dose that does not produce symptoms in normal animals) is followed by abundant secretion of saliva, convulsions, coma and death.   Houssay has shown that pancreatectomy produces an intense diabetes in toads.   If the pituitary is removed, pancreatectomy does not give rise to glycosuria and the blood sugar shows no increase.   If now an anterior lobe is implanted beneath the skin there develops an intense diabetes with glycosuria and hyperglycemia.   Barnes (8a) also points out that spontaneous glycosuria has not been observed in a hypophysectomized pancreatectomized dog; but glycosuria can be produced at will by injection of anterior pituitary lobe extracts.   He has also produced glycosuria in normal dogs by the injection of anterior pituitary extracts.

Lactogenic hormone[8]

Corner (17) in 1930 pointed out that the corpus luteum is not essential for lactation, but that the secretion of milk is brought about by one of the pituitary hormones.   Riddle (73) (75) has apparently obtained an extract of the anterior pituitary (to which the name *prolactin* has been given) which provokes the effective stimulus for the enlargement and functioning (formation of "crop-milk") of the crop-glands in pigeons.   The hormone may be prepared relatively free from the growth and gonad-stimulating principles by suspending a quantity of desiccated anterior lobe powder, or of ground fresh anterior lobes in a volume of water equal to 10 to 15 times its dry weight. N sodium hydroxide is added until the pH is 8.5 to 9.0.   After stirring for one hour, the mixture is centrifuged, the supernatent liquid decanted, and the insoluble portion suspended in water at the original volume and extracted for one hour.   The extractions are repeated 4 to 5 times, sodium hydroxide being added each time after the first two extracts until the pH of the last extract is 10.5 to 11.0.   The alkaline insoluble residue (A) is brought to pH 5 to 7 with hydrochloric acid and is then dried with alcohol and acetone.   The first pH 9.0 extract is ad-

[8] For a general discussion, see Turner (87a).

justed at once to about pH 8.0 and centrifuged. The pH 8.0-insoluble fraction from this is suspended in the second extract of the powder, again adjusted to about pH 8.0 and centrifuged. This pH 8-insoluble fraction is similarly extracted with each succeeding alkaline extract. The final pH 8-insoluble fraction (B) is suspended in a small volume of water, adjusted to pH 5 to 6 with hydrochloric acid and dried with alcohol and acetone.

The pH 8-soluble fractions are adjusted in turn to the point of minimum solubility (isoelectric point?) at pH 5.0 to 5.5 and centrifuged. This isoelectric precipitate is suspended in, and thereby extracted with, each subsequent pH 8-soluble fraction as the latter is precipitated isoelectrically. The combined iso-insoluble factions (C) are dried with alcohol and acetone. The first two or three iso-soluble fractions (containing most of the gonad-stimulating hormone) are combined (the other soluble fractions may be discarded), concentrated *in vacuo* to one-tenth their original volume and precipitated with 75 per cent alcohol. After standing, the supernatent liquid is decanted and the precipitate dried. This precipitate is extracted with water (containing a small quantity of sodium hydroxide), reprecipitating at the isoelectric point, centrifuging, decanting the soluble fraction and again extracting the iso-insoluble fraction (D). The iso-soluble fraction from D is precipitated with 70 to 75 per cent alcohol and the precipitate dried. This is iso-soluble fraction E.

The pH 11-insoluble residue (A), contains no gonad-stimulating potency and only traces of prolactin. The pH 8-insoluble fraction (B) contains little gonad-stimulating hormone and is about one-fourth as potent in prolactin as fraction (C). The main iso-insoluble fraction (C) is the prolactin fraction. It contains little gonad-stimulating hormone. (D) is as potent in prolactin as (C) but may contain more gonad-stimulating hormone. Iso-soluble fraction E is a potent gonad-stimulating hormone and contains but a trace of prolactin.

"It is thus seen that prolactin is obtained chiefly from insoluble residues which have been discarded by those who have hitherto made preparations of the growth and gonad-stimulating hormones."

By the use of alkaline extracts of the anterior pituitary, E. I. Evans (28) has induced copious lactation in three virgin goats and one dry goat. Just what these "alkaline extracts" contain is not clear at the moment.

Gardner and Turner (44a) suggest the following method of preparation: Grind or macerate pituitaries. Add two volumes of distilled water. Add 10 per cent NaOH with constant stirring until a pH of 8.4 to 9.6 is reached. Allow the extract to stand at ice box temperatures for 24 to 36 hours. Centrifuge—a semi-gelatinous mass of tissue and a viscous, turbid fluid are obtained. Add small amounts of distilled water to the tissue and recentrifuge several times. Add the fluid removed following (6) to the original fluid obtained. Add 10 per cent HCl to the fluid portion to reduce pH to 7.4 to 7.6. Centrifuge—a considerable volume of precipitated material is removed. Wash this precipitate with successive additions of distilled water and add washings to the fluid portions first obtained. (This precipitate is toxic when neutralized and injected. Up to the present time it has been found ineffective in stimulating lactation.) Add acid to the fluid portion obtained from (9) until a pH of 7 is reached. Centrifuge—wash the precipitate and add the washings to the clear fluid obtained. (Both the solution and the precipitate contain the active material.) Add more acid to reduce the pH to approximately 5.5. A flocculent white precipitate forms. (This precipitate contains a large amount of active material. The solution remaining is inactive.) Tricresol is added at the rate of 0.4 per cent by volume to all suspensions and solutions kept for injection.

The active constituent is called *galactin*.

Adrenalotropic hormone

Evans (29) points to a pituitary hormone which probably stands in intimate relation to the adrenals. The ablation of the pituitary causes a striking atrophy of the cortex of the adrenal. Improvement is brought about by the injection of an aqueous alkaline extract of the anterior pituitary; but so far it has not yet been definitely shown that such improvement is due to a specific hormone.

THE URINE OF PREGNANCY

Anterior pituitary-like substances have been prepared from the urine of pregnancy (see Zondek's method, p. 72);[9] but the material obtained from the urine of pregnancy and that obtained from the anterior pituitary are probably different. Evans (32) points out that prolan does not easily repair the gonadal deficiencies of hypophysectomized animals, whereas hypophysical hormones are completely effective in this respect. (See, also, Smith (79).) The placenta is perhaps the source of the hormones found in pregnancy urine (25).

The pregnancy test

This test, based upon the discharge of an anterior pituitary-like substance into the urine during pregnancy, has been extensively discussed since Aschheim and Zondek announced their important discovery (7). In this chapter we have referred to the test several times, even though somewhat indirectly. The biologist and the clinician, who are interested in the practical details of the test, will find them in Mazur and Goldstein's volume (63), to name but one up-to-date text. Aschheim, one of the authors of the test, has published a small book on the subject (8). (See, also, Zondek's volume (101).) While a discussion of this justly famous test is beyond the scope of this volume, references to

[9] Friedman uses the rabbit as a test animal; here ovulation can be induced by a single intravenous injection of pregnant urine (40).

several articles dealing with it are given: (94) (10) (41) (64) (78) (70) (21) (23).

Active extracts from the urine of pregnancy

We shall give several of the most recent methods for the preparation of active extracts from the urine of pregnancy.

Funk (43) and Katzman and Doisy (51) precipitate the active material by adsorption on benzoic acid.[10] The urine (preserved with a little chloroform and kept in the cold room at 1° to 5°C.) is made acid to methyl red-methylene blue by the addition of glacial acetic acid and filtered. While the urine is vigorously stirred with a mechanical stirrer, a saturated solution of benzoic acid in acetone (50 cc. per liter of urine) is added. The material is allowed to remain in the cold room overnight. The precipitate is filtered off and dissolved in a volume of acetone equal to the volume originally added. The solution is centrifuged and the small amount of undissolved material (which is the active substance) is washed thoroughly with acetone (to remove traces of benzoic acid and theelin) and extracted three times with distilled water, centrifuging after each extraction. For 1 liter of urine 25 cc. of water is used (and for 100 liters, 300 to 500 cc. water).

Cinnamic acid can be effectively used as a substitute for benzoic acid; "but the difference in cost makes the latter preferable." Tungstic acid can also be used (52a).

Further purification of the active material may be accomplished by fractional precipitation with acetone: from concentrated solutions the hormone is precipitated when the acetone concentration is between 50 to 60 per cent.

Doisy defines his mouse unit as the minimum quantity of material which, administered subcutaneously to 19-day-old mice in six equal portions during the course of three days,

---

[10] A good review of earlier methods of preparation will be found in Doisy's paper.

causes opening of the vagina and estrus on the twenty-second to twenty-fourth day of age. When 21-day-old rats are used, 1 rat unit must produce these reactions by the twenty-seventh day.

To make sure that the ovary-stimulating hormone is not mixed with some estrogenic hormones (which can induce the phenomena just described), the adult spayed female rat (on which the stimulating factor is without effect) should also be used.

By fractional precipitation with acetone the potency of the extracts have been increased from 1250 mouse units per milligram of solids to 3000 mouse units.

Katzman and Doisy (51) have also prepared a hormone extract by adsorbing the active substance on norit, eluting with 90 per cent phenol and separating the hormone from the phenol by dissolving the latter in alcohol. Haurowitz (71) and Fischer (39) have also used an adsorption method: in their case they adsorb the hormone on kaolin and elute with dilute ammonium hydroxide. The precipitation of the hormone with uranyl acetate (71) and with sulfosalicylic acid (95) has also been advocated.

Van Dyke (90) prepares his *hebin* from the urine of pregnant women by first bringing it to a pH 4.5 with glacial acetic acid, then concentrating the liquid at room temperature by placing it in front of a fan. The concentrated material is centrifuged and enough alcohol is added to the supernatant liquid to bring the volume up to 75 per cent. The precipitate, which contains the active material, is dissolved in water (one-twelfth the volume of the original urine), centrifuged, and alcohol is again added to the supernatant fluid until the volume reaches 75 per cent. The material is allowed to stand for some time and then centrifuged. The precipitate is washed with 95 per cent alcohol, then with ether and alcohol. The precipitate is redissolved in water (one-fortieth the volume of the original urine). If desired, the yellow color of the solution can be removed with norit. It seems to be less stable than the *hebin* prepared from the pituitary.

A careful consideration of various factors to be observed in the preparation of an active extract led Elden (24) to the following procedure: 2.5 per cent, by weight, of powdered willow charcoal or kaolin is added to the urine of pregnancy, after adjusting to a pH of 4.2 (with brom-phenol blue). The product is allowed to stand in the refrigerator overnight with occasional stirring, then centrifuged, and the charcoal or kaolin is washed with a small quantity of distilled water, and the hormone is extracted by treating with 0.1 N sodium hydroxide in the refrigerator overnight. The charcoal is separated by centrifugation and the supernatent extract injected.

The virgin female rabbit weighing 5 to 6 pounds was used as the test animal. The extract was injected intravenously and 18 hours later a laparotomy was performed under intra-peritoneal amytal anesthesia. A positive ovulation test, according to Friedman (40), was taken to indicate the presence of the hormone. The smallest amount necessary to cause ovulation in at least six rabbits was determined; this amount was called one rabbit unit.

Elden (24) shows that heat concentration even at 35° and reduced pressure causes a loss of 70 per cent of the hormone, and the product is toxic in most cases; that alcohol precipitation causes a loss of 60 to 75 per cent, yielding a product which is often toxic; that the addition of ammonium sulfate causes a loss of 60 to 70 per cent, but a non-toxic product is obtained; and that finally adsorption and extraction yield 50 per cent of the hormone, with no accompanying toxicity.

According to Elden, in fairly concentrated preparations, the biuret and Millon tests are negative. This result is not in accord with the findings of a number of other investigators. After adsorption and extraction of the active material, it is no longer precipitated by alcohol, acetone or ammonium sulfate.

In attempts to recover the hormone as completely as possible, two methods of extraction have been proposed recently. In one of them (19), Lloyd's reagent is used as the adsorbent, and aqueous pyridine or alkalinized acetone as the eluent. The urine is brought to pH 5 with glacial acetic acid, filtered and shaken for two hours with 20 grams of Lloyd's reagent per liter. The solution is readjusted to pH 5 and filtered by suction. The urine is discarded. Fifty per cent aqueous pyridine (in amount equal to the volume of the urine) is added to the adsorbent in a flask and shaken continuously for 8 hours. The solvent is removed by filtration or centrifugation. The extraction with pyridine is repeated. The residue is washed with small amounts of 33 per cent acetone, and the washings are added to the extracts. (If alkaline acetone is used in place of aqueous pyridine, mix equal parts of c.p. acetone and 0.2 N NaOH, and extract as with pyridine, except that extractions are limited to 4 hours. Wash with 33 per cent acetone.) The combined extracts are poured into 16 volumes of acetone at 38°C. The material is kept at about 8°C. until the precipitate has subsided. The liquor is siphoned off, and the container with the precipitate is placed in the breeze of a fan to remove the rest of the acetone. The dried precipitate is taken up with water or with saline solution for injection.

The minimal effective dose of untreated urine is considered to be the least amount of that urine which injected in 5 daily portions produces in at least one of 3 rats, 24 days of age at the beginning of the injections, a 100 per cent increase in ovary weight and one or more corpora lutea at necropsy on the sixth day. Approximately duplicate ovarian effects are produced by the minimal effective dose of the whole urine and by an equivalent amount of the extract, pointing to the effectiveness of the extraction process. The extract is free from theelin, since it is without effect on the uteri of immature castrate female rats.

In the other method (52), tungstic acid is selected as the precipitant. This acid is so efficient that by its means the authors have been able to detect the presence of the hormone in normal urine. 10 cc. of 10 per cent sodium tungstate and 10 cc. of 0.5 per cent casein (the casein helps adsorption) are added to a 24-hour sample of urine, which is then made faintly acid to congo red with dilute sulfuric acid. The precipitate is collected by centrifugation, washed with acetone, freed from acetone by reduced pressure, and dissolved by adding dilute sodium hydroxide until the mixture is faintly alkaline to phenolphthalein. Barium chloride and barium hydroxide are then added in the proportion necessary to prevent the solution from becoming acid, until precipitation is complete. The precipitate is removed by centrifugation, and the excess barium is precipitated by sodium sulfate, the barium sulfate removed and the solution neutralized with dilute acetic acid.

Hormone added in as small as 4.4 mouse units per liter can be recovered by this procedure. Between the ages of 4 years and puberty little or no anterior pituitary-like hormone is found in the urine, but at puberty an increased excretion occurs.

Very recently Zondek (105) has succeeded in obtaining very active fractions of his prolan from the urine of pregnancy. (For a complete summary of his earlier work, see (101).) Reminding his reader that in the various methods proposed for preparing active extracts, one must keep in mind the sensitivity of prolan to temperature (not above 50°), to acids and to alkalis, he proposes the following procedure:

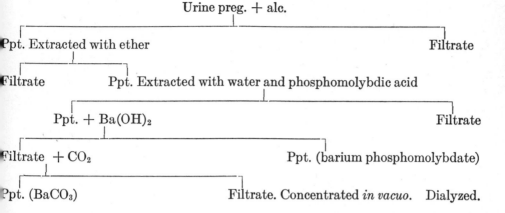

Urine preg. + alc.

Ppt. Extracted with ether   Filtrate

Filtrate   Ppt. Extracted with water and phosphomolybdic acid

Ppt. + Ba(OH)$_2$ Filtrate

Filtrate + CO$_2$ Ppt. (barium phosphomolybdate)

Ppt. (BaCO$_3$)   Filtrate. Concentrated *in vacuo.*   Dialyzed.

THE POSTERIOR LOBE

Despite the large amount of work done in this field, the situation is still not very satisfactory. (Good reviews of the earlier literature will be found in the papers by Abel (1) (2), Geiling (45) and Kamm (50) (11).) Aqueous acid extracts of this gland (*pituitrin*) exhibit various physiological properties (cardio-vascular, plain muscle and melanophore stimulating, diuretic-antidiuretic, respiratory, etc.). There has been much dispute as to whether these various effects are the result of the activity of one or more hormones. Abel and his associates have advocated the existence of but one hormone. Dudley, among others, has strenuously opposed this view (22). Kamm in 1928 apparently definitely settled the dispute by showing that two active fractions, an oxytocic principle and a pressor principle, can be separated.

Commercial pituitary solutions contain "the water-soluble principle or principles from the fresh posterior lobe of the pituitary body of cattle, 1 cc. having an activity upon the isolated uterus of the virgin guinea pig corresponding to not less than 80 per cent and not more than 120 per cent of that produced by 0.005 gram of the standard pituitary powder" (88) (66). A solution the potency of which is such that each cubic centimeter is derived from 5 mg. of the standard powder may also be expressed in International Units (League of Nations), each cubic centimeter being equivalent to 10 International Oxytocic Units. One milligram of the U. S. P. Standard Powdered Pituitary is equal to two International Units of oxytocic activity (50).

The "standard pituitary powder" is prepared from fresh posterior lobes (within 30 minutes after death) from which all extraneous tissue is removed. Four cubic centimeters of acetone is added for each pituitary body. The material is allowed to stand for three hours, then removed and cut into small pieces and once more put into the same volume of fresh acetone, with which it is left in contact overnight. The product is now dried in a vacuum desiccator for five hours at a temperature not above 50°C. It is now ground, again dried, but this time for twelve hours, extracted in a Soxhlet for three hours, and once again dried for twelve hours. This dried powder is used to prepare the standard solution.

This solution is prepared by extracting the powder with 0.25 per cent acetic acid. (The final volume of the mixture should contain the same number of cubic centimeters as the number of milligrams of the dried powder originally taken.) The mixture is heated to boiling for one minute and filtered. Each cubic centimeter of the filtrate contains the active principle of 0.001 gram of powder. It is sterilized by fractional sterilization for twenty minutes on three successive days at a temperature not above 100°C.

For assay, the uterus of a guinea pig is used. Varying doses of the standard extract and of the solution to be tested are added to the bath in the muscle chamber until quantities of the two solutions are found which give equal contractions. The strengths of the solution are in inverse ratio to the quantities necessary to produce these equal contractions (66, p. 637).

Abel and his associates have prepared a product from the pars intermedia and the posterior lobe which, in the form of a tartrate salt, exhibits, according to them, "all the manifold characteristic physiological actions of the posterior lobe" (1) (2). Two "minor substances," one of them histamine, have also been isolated among the fractions; but these are not considered to be part of the true hormone of the lobe.

The isolation of the active principle is rather involved. The glands are extracted with weak (0.35 per cent) hydrochloric acid containing mercuric chloride (4 grams for 100 grams of pituitary paste). The material is stirred for several hours. The "two minor products" are found in the supernatant fluid, whilst the principle product is adsorbed on the mercuric chloride-protein precipitate. The precipitate is ground with water, neutralized to litmus, treated with hydrogen sulfide and filtered. The filtrate is aerated to remove the excess of hydrogen sulfide, and phosphotungstic acid is added until the precipitation is complete.

The phosphotungstate precipitate is decomposed with barium hydroxide, the barium phosphotungstate filtered off, the excess barium in the filtrate removed as sulfate, and the active principle in the filtrate is precipitated with tannic acid. The tannate precipitate is dissolved in alcohol, tartaric acid is added, and the tartrate is precipitated by the addition of an excess of ether. (Further purification with picrolonic acid is possible.)

Some of these tartrate preparations, in their action on smooth muscle tissues, are from 1000 to 1250 times more powerful than histamine. In addition to their oxytocic action, the tartrates cause prolonged rise in the arterial blood pressure; a brief diuresis in the green-fed rabbit; an antidiuretic action in diabetes insipidus; and effects the respiration of rabbits, as also the breathing and the heart of unanesthetized dogs, in a characteristic manner. "These manifold actions, namely oxytocic, pressor, diuretic-antidiuretic, respiratory and cardiac, are all obtained in high dilution with the purified tartrate.''

Dudley, in attempts to purify the oxytocic principle, isolated the inert potassium creatinine picrate and, in examining the mother liquor, came to the conclusion that there were at least three definite physiologically active substances: an oxytocic principle and two pressor principles (22); a view which is, of course, very definitely opposed to Abel's. Dudley uses butyl alcohol to separate the oxytocic from the pressor principle. Abel claims that his pituitary tartrate is soluble in butyl alcohol and that this solvent fails to separate his product into two distinct fractions (45).

But a much more serious objection to Abel's work comes from the recent labors of Kamm (50), who has, apparently, shown the presence of two active principles. The oxytocic principle (*oxytocin*), is given the name *alpha-hypophamine*, or *pitocin*, and the pressor principle (*vasopressin*) is called *beta-hypophamine*, or *pitressin*.

In the preparation of his active principles (50) (11), the posterior lobes are desiccated with acetone and extracted with 0.25 per cent acetic, as already described (p. 104). The filtrate is concentrated at a low temperature, and the active materials, together with proteins, are precipitated by the addition of ammonium sulfate. Extraction of the precipitate with glacial acetic acid leaves behind most of the inert proteins. The acetic acid extract is treated with ether and then with petroleum ether, which causes a precipitation of the active material (A). At this stage 90 to 95 per cent of the inert material has been removed.

The separation of the oxytocic from the pressor principle depends upon the fact that the former is appreciably soluble in organic solvents, particularly in a mixture of ether and acetic acid. The precipitate (A) is therefore dissolved in acetic acid and reprecipitated with ether. This is repeated. The ether filtrate contains the oxytocic activity (B). (B) is concentrated and purified by precipitating with petroleum ether.

The partially purified precipitate (A), which has been twice dissolved in acetic acid and precipitated with ether, can be further purified by dissolving it in acetic acid and adding acetone. The precipitate consists mainly of protein. The filtrate is treated with more acetone and more inert protein separates out. The filtrate now obtained is treated with ether. The precipitate is very active by the pressor test but less active by the oxytocic test. The filtrate is now treated with an excess of ether in order to precipitate the remainder of the pressor activity. The filtrate now obtained contains only a trace of pressor activity but the bulk of the oxytocic activity. The latter may be obtained by the addition of petroleum ether.

Further purifications are obtained by repeating the type of fractionations outlined here.

As showing the efficiency of these fractionations, the following table is illuminating:

	Ratio of pressor to oxytocic activity
Second fractionation	100:60
Third fractionation	100:24
Fourth fractionation	100:14
Fifth fractionation	100:12
Sixth fractionation	100:10
Seventh fractionation	100: 8.5

"The separate fractions may be recombined, dissolved in acidified water, and diluted back to the original volume, yielding a solution that is indistinguishable from the original gland extract."

The method of assay for oxytocic principle, making use of the contraction of a guinea-pig's uterus, has already been referred to (p. 104). For determining the pressor activity, the carotid arteries of dogs are cannulated and connected to mercury manometers which record on smoked paper.

Doses of standard pituitrin are injected into the saphenous veins and then doses of the unknown solution are similarly injected. The dosages are varied until equal rises in blood pressure are obtained with standard solution and unknown solution.

The darkening of the skin of frogs and tadpoles by the use of pituitrin is now shown to be due to the pressor principle; and the well-known diuretic-antidiuretic action of pituitrin is also shown to be due to the pressor principle. "Vasopressin has been used . . . for the treatment of diabetes insipidus . . . and oxytocin has been tested and found to cause contractions of the uterus in such a degree that it may be used in place of pituitrin in obstetrical practice."

In the form of their final products, the pressor principle (a white, stable, water-soluble powder) is 80 times as potent as the International Standard Powdered Pituitary; and the oxytocic principle (also a white, stable, water-soluble powder) is 150 times as potent as the International Standard.

Stehle (83a) suggests the following method for separating pressor and oxytocic substances: Inert material is first removed with alcohol and then with barium hydroxide, ferric sulfate and colloidal iron. The concentrate obtained is dissolved in dilute alcohol and the solution is fractionally precipitated with ethyl acetate. The fractions are further purified by utilizing the different distribution of the substances between the two phases of a water-alcohol-ethyl acetate system, the pressor substance entering the aqueous phase and the oxytocic substance concentrating in the ethyl acetate phase.

For several clinical references to pituitrin (or its components), see (66) (63) (47) (83) (96) (84).

REFERENCES

(1) ABEL, J. J.: Physiological, chemical and clinical studies on pituitary principles. *Harvey Lectures* (Lippincott, Philadelphia. 1923–1924), p. 154.

(2) ABEL, J. J.: The chemistry and function of the pituitary gland. *Ind. and Eng. Chem.*, **16**, 1031 (1924).

(3) ANDERSON, E. M., AND COLLIP, J. B.: Thyreotropic hormone of anterior pituitary. *Proc. Soc. Exp. Biol. and Med.*, **30**, 680 (1933).

(4) ANON.: Estrogenic substances. *J. Am. Med. Assoc.*, **100**, 1331 (1933).

(5) ANSELMINO, K. J., AND HOFFMANN, F.: Das Fettstoffwechselhormon des Hypophysenvorderlappens. I. Nachweis, Darstellung und Eigenschaften des Hormons. *Klin. Woch.*, **10**, 2380 (1931).

(6) ANSELMINO, K. J., AND HOFFMANN, F.: Darstellung, Eigenschaften und Vorkommen einer Antithyreoiden Schutzsubstanz aus Blut und Geweben. *Klin. Woch.*, **12**, 99 (1933).

(7) ASCHHEIM, S., AND ZONDEK, B.: Die Schwangerschaftsdiagnose aus dem Harn durch Nachweis des Hypophysenvorderlappenhormons. *Klin. Woch.*, **7**, 1401 (1928).

(8) ASCHHEIM, S.: Die Schwangerschaftsdiagnose aus dem Harne (Aschheim-Zondek-Reaktion). (Karger, Berlin. 1930.)

(8a) BARNES, B. O., AND REGAN, J. F.: The relation of the anterior pituitary to carbohydrate metabolism. *Endocrinology*, **17**, 522 (1933).

(9) BENGTSON, B. N.: Pituitary therapy of alopecia. *J. Am. Med. Assoc.*, **97**, 1355 (1931).

(10) BROUHA, L., HINGLAIS, H., AND SIMONNET, T.: L'action de l'urine de femme enceinte sur le tractus génital de la souris. *Bull. Acad. de Méd. Paris*, **103**, 150 (1930).

(11) BUGBEE, E. P., AND KAMM, O.: Recent progress in the investigation of the posterior lobe of the pituitary gland. *Endocrinology*, **12**, 671 (1928).

(12) BUGBEE, E. P., SIMOND, A. E., AND GRIMES, H. M.: Anterior pituitary hormones. *Endocrinology*, **15**, 41 (1931).

(13) CALDER, R. M.: Pituitary cachexia (Simmond's disease) treated with anterior pituitary extract. *J. Am. Med. Assoc.*, **98**, 314 (1932).

(14) CALDER, R. M.: Anterior pituitary insufficiency. *Bull. Johns Hopkins Hospital*, **50**, 87 (1932).

(15) CLOSS, K., LOEB, L., AND MACKAY, E. M.: The effect of an acid extract of the anterior pituitary on the iodine concentration of the blood and thyroid gland. *J. Biol. Chem.*, **96**, 585 (1932).

(15a) COLLIP, J. B., SELYE, H., ANDERSON, E. M., AND THOMPSON, D. L.: Production of estrus. Relationship between active principles of the placenta and pregnancy blood and urine and those of the anterior pituitary. *J. Am. Med. Assoc.*, **101**, 1553 (1933).

(16) COLLIP, J. B., SELYE, H., AND THOMSON, D. L.: Preparation of a purified and highly potent extract of growth hormone of anterior pituitary lobe. *Proc. Soc. Exp. Biol. and Med.*, **30**, 544 (1933).

(17) CORNER, G. W.: The hormonal control of lactation. I. Non-effect of the corpus luteum. II. Positive action of extracts of the hypophysis. *Am. J. Physiol.*, **15**, 43 (1930).

(18) CREW, F. A. E., AND WIESNER, B. P.: On the existence of a fourth hormone, thyreotropic in nature, of the anterior pituitary. *Brit. Med. J.*, p. 777 (1930).

(18a) CUSHING, H.: "Dyspituitarism:" twenty years later. *Harvey Lectures* (Williams & Wilkins, Baltimore, 1934), p. 90.

(19) DAVY, L., AND SEVRINGHAUS, E. L.: Complete recovery of gonadotropic substances from urine of women. *Proc. Soc. Exp. Biol. and Med.*, **30**, 1422 (1933).

(20) DINGEMANSE, E., AND DE JONGH, S. E.: Die Mehrheit der Sexualhormone der Hypophyse; Wirkung auf weibliche Tiere. *Pflüger's Archiv.*, **226**, 543 (1930).

(21) DORN, J. H., AND SUGARMAN, E. I.: A method for the prediction of sex in the unborn. *J. Am. Med. Assoc.*, **99**, 1659 (1932).

(22) DUDLEY, H. W.: Active principles of pituitary gland. *J. Pharmacol.*, **21**, 77 (1923).

(23) EBERSON, F., AND SILVERBERG, M. H.: Anterior pituitary hormone in urine. *J. Am. Med. Assoc.*, **96**, 2176 (1931).

(24) ELDEN, C. A.: A method of separating the anterior pituitary-like hormone from the urine of pregnant women. *J. Biol. Chem.*, **101**, 1 (1933).

(25) ENGLE, E. T.: Effects of extracts of the anterior pituitary and similar active principles of blood and urine. In Allen's *Sex and Internal Secretions*. (Williams & Wilkins, Baltimore. 1932), p. 765.

(26) ENGLE, E. T.: Differences in response of female macacus monkey to extracts of anterior pituitary and of human pregnancy urine. *Proc. Soc. Exp. Biol. and Med.*, **30**, 530 (1933).

(27) EVANS, E. I.: Initiation of copious milk secretion in virgin goats by anterior pituitary. *Proc. Soc. Exp. Biol. and Med.*, **30**, 1372 (1933).

(28) EVANS, H. M.: The functions of the anterior hypophysis. *Harvey Lectures* (Lippincott, Philadelphia. 1923–1924), p. 212.

(29) EVANS, H. M.: Present position of our knowledge of anterior pituitary function. *J. Am. Med. Assoc.*, **101**, 425 (1933).

(30) EVANS, H. M., CORNISH, R. E., AND SIMPSON, M. E.: Potent, sterile and low-protein extracts of the growth hormone from the anterior hypophysis. *Proc. Soc. Exp. Biol. & Med.*, **27**, 101 (1929).

(31) EVANS, H. M., AND LONG, J. A.: The effect of the anterior pituitary lobe administered intraperitoneally upon growth, maturity and oestrus cycles of the rat. *Anat. Rec.*, **21**, 62 (1921).

(32) EVANS, H. M., MEYER, K., AND SIMPSON, M. E.: Relation of prolan to the anterior hypophyseal hormones. *Am. J. Physiol.*, **100**, 141 (1932).

(33) EVANS, H. M., MEYER, K., SIMPSON, M. E., AND REICHERT, F. L.: Disturbance of carbohydrate metabolism in normal dogs injected with the hypophyseal growth hormone. *Proc. Soc. Exp. Biol. and Med.*, **29**, 857 (1932).

(34) Evans, H. M., and Simpson, M. E.: Antagonism of growth and sex hormones of the anterior hypophysis. *J. Am. Med. Assoc.*, **91**, 1337 (1928).

(35) Evans, H. M., and Simpson, M. E.: Hormones of the anterior hypophysis. *Am. J. Physiol.*, **98**, 511 (1931).

(35a) Evans, H. M., Simpson, M. E., Austin, P. R., and Fergusson, R. S.: Peculiarities of the prolan-like substance in urine in a case of embryonal carcinoma of the testis. *Proc. Soc. Exp. Biol. and Med.*, **31**, 21 (1933).

(36) Fevold, H. L.: The chemical nature of the ovarian and the gonadotropic hormones. *J. Chem. Educ.*, **10**, 174 (1933).

(37) Fevold, H. L., Hisaw, F. L., Hellbaum, A., and Hertz, R.: Further purification of a follicular stimulating factor and the physiological effects on immature rats and rabbits. *Am. J. Physiol.*, **104**, 710 (1933).

(38) Fevold, H. L., Hisaw, F. L., and Leonard, S. L.: The gonad-stimulating and the luteinizing hormones of the anterior lobe of the hypophyses. *Am. J. Physiol.*, **97**, 291 (1931).

(39) Fischer, F. G., and Ertel, L.: Zur kenntnis der Hypophysenvorderlappen-Hormone aus Schwangerenharn. *Zt. physiol. Chem.*, **202**, 83 (1931).

(40) Friedman, M. H.: Mechanism of ovulation in the rabbit. II. Ovulation produced by the injection of urine from pregnant women. *Am. J. Physiol.*, **90**, 617 (1929).

(41) Friedman, M. H., and Lapham, M. E.: A simple, rapid procedure for the laboratory diagnosis of early pregnancies. *Am. J. Obst. and Gynec.*, **21**, 405 (1931).

(42) Funk, C.: Further experiments on the fat metabolism hormone obtained from normal urine. *Proc. Am. Soc. Biol. Chem.*, **8**, 43 (1933).

(43) Funk, C., and Zefirow, P.: Preparation of gonadotropic hormones from normal urine and urine of pregnancy. *Biochem. J.*, **26**, 619 (1932).

(44) Funk, C., and Zefirow, P. P.: The hormone of fat metabolism of the anterior pituitary. *Archivio di Scienze Biologiche*, **18**, 142 (1933).

(44a) Gardner, W. U., and Turner, C. W.: Galactin, a lactation-stimulating hormone of the anterior pituitary. *Mo. Agr. Expt. Sta.*, *Research Bull.*, **195**, 5 (1933).

(45) Geiling, E. M. K.: The pituitary body. *Physiol. Rev.*, **6**, 62 (1926).

(46) Greep, R.: Effect of luteinizing and follicular stimulating fractions of the pituitary on the thyroid. *Proc. Soc. Exp. Biol. and Med.*, **30**, 1362 (1933).

(47) Grollman, A., and Geiling, E. M. K.: The cardiovascular and metabolic reactions of man to the intramuscular injection of posterior pituitary liquid (pituitrin), pitressin and pitocin. *J. Pharmacol.*, **46**, 447 (1932).

(48) HOFFMANN, F., AND ANSELMINO, K. J.: Das Fettstoffwechselhormon des Hypophysenvorderlappens. II. Stoffwechselswirkungen und Regulationen des Hormons. *Klin. Woch.*, **10**, 2383 (1931).

(49) HOUSSAY, B. A., AND BIASOTTI, A.: The hypophysis, carbohydrate metabolism and diabetes. *Endocrinology*, **15**, 511 (1931).

(50) KAMM, O., ALDRICH, T. B., GROTE, I. W., ROWE, L. W., AND BUGBEE, E. P.: The active principles of the posterior lobe of the pituitary gland. I. The demonstration of the presence of two active principles. II. The separation of the two principles and their concentration in the form of potent solid preparations. *J. Am. Chem. Soc.*, **50**, 573 (1928).

(51) KATZMAN, P. A., AND DOISY, E. A.: Preparation of extracts of the anterior pituitary-like substance of urine of pregnancy. *J. Biol. Chem.*, **98**, 739 (1932).

(52) KATZMAN, P. A., AND DOISY, E. A.: A quantitative procedure for determining normal excretion of prolan. *Proc. Soc. Exp. Biol. and Med.*, **30**, 1188 (1933).

(52a) KATZMAN, P. A., AND DOISY, E. A.: Preparation of gonadotropic substance by tungstic acid precipitation. *Proc. Soc. Exp. Biol. and Med.*, **31**, 188 (1933).

(53) KROGH, M., AND OKKELS, H.: The thyroid-stimulating hormone from the anterior pituitary. Some chemical properties. *Archivio di Scienze Biologiche*, **18**, 214 (1933).

(54) LEONARD, S. L.: The nature of the substance causing ovulation in the rabbit. *Am. J. Physiol.*, **98**, 406 (1931).

(55) LEONARD, S. L.: Differences between human anterior pituitary extracts and prolan. *Proc. Soc. Exp. Biol. and Med.*, **30**, 1251 (1933).

(56) LOEB, L.: The specificity in the action of the anterior pituitary of different mammals as well as of urine of pregnant women on the sex organs and thyroid glands of immature female guinea pigs. *Endocrinology*, **16**, 129 (1932).

(57) LOEB, L., AND BASSETT, R. B.: Effect of hormones of anterior pituitary on thyroid gland in the guinea-pig. *Proc. Soc. Exp. Biol. & Med.*, **26**, 860 (1929).

(58) LOEB, L., AND BASSETT, R. B.: Comparison of effects of various preparations of anterior pituitary gland on thyroid of guinea pig. *Proc. Soc. Exp. Biol. and Med.*, **27**, 490 (1930).

(59) LOEB, L., AND FRIEDMAN, H.: The two main types of anterior pituitary gland present in different species of animals *Proc. Soc. Exp. Biol. and Med.*, **30**, 741 (1933).

(60) LOESER, A.: Eigenschaften und Haltbarkeit des Hypophysenvorderlappenpulvers. *Archiv. f. Exp. Pathol. und Pharmakol.*, **161**, 730 (1931).

(61) LOESER, A.: Methode zur darstellung Thyreotrop wirksamer extrakte aus Hypophysenvorderlappen. *Klin. Woch.*, **11**, 1271 (1932).

(62) MARINE, D., AND ROSEN, S. H.: Exophthalmos in thyroidectomised guinea pigs by thyrotropic substance of anterior pituitary, and the mechanism involved. *Proc. Soc. Exp. Biol. and Med.*, **30**, 901 (1933).

(63) MAZUR, C., AND GOLDSTEIN, L.: Clinical Endocrinology of the Female. (Saunders, Philadelphia. 1932.)

(64) MAZUR, C., AND HOFFMAN, J.: The three hormone tests for early pregnancy. *J. Am. Med. Assoc.*, **96**, 19 (1931).

(64a) MAZUR, C., AND KATZ, B. R.: Clinical evaluation of combined prolan and anterior pituitary therapy. *Endocrinology*, **17**, 709 (1933).

(65) MOORE, C. R., AND PRICE, D.: Gonad hormone functions, and the reciprocal influence between gonads and hypophysis with its bearing on the problem of sex-hormone antagonism. *Am. J. Anat.*, **50**, 13 (1932).

(66) MUNCH, J. C.: Bioassays. (Williams & Wilkins, Baltimore. 1931.)

(67) PARVEY, B.: Recent advances in the physiology of reproduction in relation to the Zondek-Aschheim test for the early detection of pregnancy. *Endocrinology*, **16**, 225 (1932).

(68) PUTNAM, T. J., TEEL, H. M., AND BENEDICT, E. M.: The preparation of a sterile active extract from the anterior lobe of the hypophysis. *Am. J. Physiol.*, **84**, 157 (1928).

(69) REICHERT, F. L.: Effects of anterior pituitary extract upon an hypophysectomized puppy. *Proc. Soc. Exp. Biol. Med.*, **27**, 204 (1929).

(70) REINHART, H. L., AND SCOTT, E.: A modification of the Aschheim-Zondek test for pregnancy. *J. Am. Med. Assoc.*, **96**, 1565 (1931).

(71) REISS, M., AND HAUROWITZ, F.: Zur chemie des Hypophysenvorderlappen-sexual-Hormons. *Z. ges. exp. Med.*, **68**, 371 (1929).

(72) REISS, M., SCHAFFNER, A., AND HAUROWITZ, F.: Ueber die Inaktivierung des aus Schwangerenharn gewonnen Hypophysenvorderlappenharmons durch proteolytische Enzyme. *Endokrinologie*, **8**, 22 (1931).

(73) RIDDLE, O., BATES, R. W., AND DYKSHORN, S. W.: A new hormone of the anterior pituitary. *Proc. Soc. Exp. Biol. and Med.*, **29**, 1211 (1932).

(74) RIDDLE, O., BATES, R. W., AND DYKSHORN, S. W.: Thyroid hypertrophy as a response to the gonad-stimulating hormone of the pituitary. *Proc. Soc. Exp. Biol. and Med.*, **30**, 794 (1933).

(75) RIDDLE, O., BATES, R. W., AND DYKSHORN, S. W.: The preparation, identification and assay of prolactin-a hormone of the anterior pituitary. *Am. J. Physiol.*, **105**, 191 (1933).

(76) SCHOCKAERT, J. A., AND FOSTER, G. L.: Influence of anterior pituitary substances on the total iodine content of the thyroid gland in the young duck. *J. Biol. Chem.*, **95**, 89 (1932).

(77) SEVRINGHAUS, E. L., AND THORNTON, M. J.: Clinical use of gonadotropic substances in women. I. Treatment of sexual immaturity with concentrated preparations from pregnancy urine. *Endocrinology*, **17**, 123 (1933).

(78) SIDDALL, A. C.: The hormone test for pregnancy. *J. Am. Med. Assoc.*, **91**, 779 (1928).

(79) SMITH, P. E.: The disabilities caused by hypophysectomy and their repair. *J. Am. Med. Assoc.*, **88**, 158 (1927).

(80) SMITH, P. E.: The experimental feeding of fresh anterior pituitary substance to the hypophysectomised rat. *Am. J. Physiol.*, **81**, 20 (1927).

(81) SMITH, P. E.: Relations of the activity of the pituitary and thyroid glands. *Harvey Lectures.* (Williams & Wilkins, Baltimore. 1929–1930), p. 128.

(82) SMITH, P. E., AND ENGLE, E. T.: Experimental evidence regarding the rôle of the anterior pituitary in the development and regulation of the genital system. *Am. J. Anat.*, **40**, 159 (1927).

(83) SOLLMANN, T. H.: Pharmacology of the pituitary gland. *J. Am. Med. Assoc.*, **83**, 1683 (1924).

(83a) STEHLE, R. L. A new method for separating pressor and oxytocic substances from the posterior lobe of the pituitary gland. *J. Biol. Chem.*, **102**, 573 (1933).

(84) STEIN, A.: The use of pituitary solution. *J. Am. Med. Assoc.*, **94**, 1428 (1930).

(85) SULZBERGER, M. B.: The pituitary hormone intermedin as the active antidiuretic in the treatment of diabetes insipidus. *J. Am. Med. Assoc.*, **100**, 1928 (1933).

(86) TEEL, H. M.: A method for purification of extracts containing the growth-promoting principle of the anterior hypophysis. *Science*, **69**, 405 (1929).

(87) TEEL, H. M., AND CUSHING, H.: Studies in the physiological properties of the growth-promoting extracts of the anterior hypophysis. *Endocrinology*, **14**, 157 (1930).

(87a) TURNER, C. W.: The mammary glands (Allen's Sex and Internal Secretions, Williams & Wilkins, Baltimore. 1932), p. 544.

(88) United States Pharmacopoeia, Tenth decennial revision, 1925.

(89) VAN DYKE, H. B., AND WALLEN-LAWRENCE, Z.: On the growth-promoting hormone of the pituitary body. *J. Pharmacol.*, **40**, 413 (1930).

(90) VAN DYKE, H. B., AND WALLEN-LAWRENCE, Z.: The gonad-stimulating substance of the anterior pituitary lobe of the pituitary body and of pregnancy urine. *J. Pharmacol.*, **43**, 93 (1931).

(91) VAN DYKE, H. B., AND WALLEN-LAWRENCE, Z.: Further observations on the gonad-stimulating principle of the anterior lobe of the pituitary body. *J. Pharmacol.*, **47**, 163 (1933).

(92) WADEHN, F.: Versuche über die Einwirkung des Wachstumshormons auf die Maus. *Biochem. Zt.*, **255**, 189 (1932).

(93) WEHEFRITZ, E., AND GIERHAKE, E.: Ueber das Vorkommen von Wachstumstoffen im Schwangerenurin. *Klin. Woch.*, **11**, 1106 (1932).

(94) WHITE, M. R., AND SEVERENCE, A. O.: Comparison of pregnancy tests. *J. Am. Med. Assoc.*, **97**, 1275 (1931).

(95) WIESNER, B. P., AND MARSHALL, P. G.: The gonadotropic hormones (*p*-factors).—I. The preparation and properties of extracts of anterior lobe, placenta, and pregnancy urine. *Quart. J. Exp. Physiol.*, **21**, 147 (1931).

(96) WILLIAMS, J. W.: The use of extracts of the pituitary gland in obstetrics. *J. Am. Med. Assoc.*, **83**, 1768 (1924).

(97) ZONDEK, B.: Ueber die Hormone des Hypophysenvorderlappens. I. Wachstumshormon, Follikelreifungshormon (Prolan A). Luteinisieiungshormon (Prolan B), Stoffweihselhormon. *Klin. Woch.*, **9**, 245 (1930).

(98) ZONDEK, B.: Ueber die Hormone des Hypophysenvorderlappens. II. Follikelreifungshormon (Prolan A)—Klimaktekium-Kastration. *Klin. Woch.*, **9**, 393 (1930).

(99) ZONDEK, B.: Ueber die Hormone des Hypophysenvorderlappens. III. Follikelreifungshormon (Prolan A) und Tumoren. *Klin. Woch.*, **9**, 679 (1930).

(100) ZONDEK, B.: Ueber die Hormone des Hypophysenvorderlappens. IV. Darstellung des Follikelreifungshormon (Prolan A)—Methodik der klinischen Harnanalyse zum Nachweis des Prolans. *Klin. Woch.*, **9**, 1207 (1930).

(101) ZONDEK, B.: Die Hormone des Ovariums und des Hypophesenvorderlappens. (Springer, Berlin. 1931.)

(102) ZONDEK, B., AND ASCHHEIM, S.: Das Hormon des Hypophysenvorderlappens. I. Testobject zum Nachweis des Hormons. *Klin. Woch.*, **6**, 248 (1927).

(103) ZONDEK, B., AND ASCHHEIM, S.: Das Hormon des Hypophysenvorderlappens. Darstellung, chemische Eigenschaften, biologische Wirkungen. *Klin. Woch.*, **7**, 831 (1928).

(104) ZONDEK, B., AND KROHN, H.: Hormon des Zwischenlappens der Hypophyse (Intermedin). *Klin. Woch.*, **11**, 1293 (1932).

(105) ZONDEK, B., SCHEIBLER, H., AND KRABBE, W.: Zur Reindarstellung des gonadotropen Hormons (Prolan). *Biochem. Zt.*, **258**, 102 (1933).

(106) ZONDEK, B., AND VAN EWEYK, C.: Zur Darstellung des Weiblichen Sexual Hormons. *Klin. Woch.*, **9**, 1437 (1930).

CHAPTER V

THE ADRENAL HORMONES

The well-known hormone of the adrenal glands, adrenaline, which, like thyroxine, has been isolated and synthesized, is found in the medulla of the gland; and the cortex, we know today, contains an even more important hormone, physiologically speaking; though it is doubtful whether it has, as yet, been isolated in the chemically pure state.

ADRENALINE

Schäfer's discovery in 1894, that an extract of the adrenal glands when injected intravenously causes a rise in blood pressure (59) gave a great impetus to the further study of the adrenals. Several years later, Abel in this country and von Fürth abroad began a series of pioneer investigations into the chemical nature of the active substance. Abel first prepared the hormone in the form of its benzoyl derivative. By saponification and precipitation with ammonia, the active principle was isolated (1) (2). The method of preparation was somewhat cumbersome and the analyses of the final product were not very convincing. Abel gave the hormone the name *epinephrine*. In the meantime, von Fürth who suspected the presence within the gland of a catechol compound, because the extracts gave a green coloration with ferric chloride, prepared insoluble lead, zinc and iron salts, without being able to obtain *suprarenine*, (the name he gave to the hormone in the crystalline form (5) (23)). The actual isolation of adrenaline we owe to Takamine (who gave it this name) and to Aldrich.

"I was visited one day in the fall of 1900," writes Abel (1), "by the Japanese chemist, J. Takamine, who examined with great interest the various compounds and salts of epinephrine that were placed before him. He inquired particularly whether I did not think it possible that my salts of epinephrine could be prepared by a simpler process than mine, more especially without the troublesome and in this case wasteful process of benzoylating extracts of an animal tissue." This was precisely what Takamine accomplished (96).

Takamine's method of preparing adrenaline is, in its essential details, still the method used to this day. The minced glands are extracted with acidulated water for 5 hours at 50° to 80°, and the temperature is next raised to 95° for 1 hour to coagulate proteins. To prevent the oxidation of the active principle, Takamine used a layer of fat floating on the surface of the liquid. He also recommends the use of an inert gas like carbon dioxide. The mass is pressed and separated from the liquid portion (which contains the active principle). The residue is again treated with acidulated water, and the process is repeated. The combined extracts are concentrated *in vacuo* and three volumes of ethyl (or methyl) alcohol are added. The inert precipitate consists of organic and inorganic substances; this is filtered off and washed with alcohol. The filtrate is evaporated *in vacuo* to get rid of the alcohol, and ammonia is added until the solution is distinctly alkaline. The product is allowed to stand for several hours, yielding a yellowish-brown precipitate, which represents the crude adrenaline. This precipitate is filtered, washed with water and dried. (Takamine states in this paper that sodium hydroxide can be used in the place of ammonia, but the former has the disadvantage in that an excess of it would tend to dissolve the hormone.) To purify the material, it is dissolved in acid, and alcohol and ether are added in sufficient quantity. The precipitate is inert. The filtrate is treated with ammonia, as already described. Takamine, as the result of his analysis of the compound, ascribes to it the formula $C_{10}H_{15}NO_3$, which we now know to be wrong.

Aldrich, at one time an assistant of Abel's, also isolated adrenaline in the chemically pure state. He published his results at about the same time as Takamine. Both men use practically the same method for the preparation of the active material; which is really not so surprising, seeing that both obtained information of a fundamental kind from Abel. But Aldrich made a notable advance: he carefully and accurately analyzed his product and gave it the formula $C_9H_{13}O_3N$—an analysis which was quickly confirmed in several European laboratories and really paved the way for further chemical studies (3) (4).

A modified method of preparing adrenaline, developed by Bertrand (18), may now be given: 600 grams of gland, with fat removed, are finely minced and mixed with 5 grams of oxalic acid and enough 95 per cent alcohol to fill brim-full a 2-liter bottle. The bottle is stoppered and shaken at intervals for two days. The proteins remain behind and the adrenaline goes into solution in the form of an oxalate. The product is filtered through cloth and pressed. The filtrate is concentrated *in vacuo* to remove the alcohol. Colored substances, lecithin, fat, etc., separate out. The mixture is shaken with petroleum ether, transferred to a separatory funnel, allowed to settle, and the lower layer (free from lipins) is drawn off and lead acetate added to it until precipitation is complete. (If an excess is added, add sulfuric acid.) The product is filtered, and the filtrate evaporated *in vacuo* to 200 cc. A slight excess of ammonia is added. The product is kept in a cool place not exposed to air. The yield is 0.8 to 1.0 gram adrenaline. To purify it, the precipitate is dissolved in 2 times its weight of 10 per cent sulfuric acid and an equal volume of alcohol is added. The mixture is filtered and the filtrate reprecipitated with ammonia.

Pauli (62), who confirmed Aldrich's analysis of adrenaline, purifies his product by converting it into the oxalate and dissolving the latter in alcohol, whereby impurities are precipitated. For example, 12 grams of crude adrenaline are mixed with 50 cc. of 85 to 90 per cent alcohol (containing 7 grams of oxalic acid). The product is filtered, the filtrate diluted to 100 cc., and the active substance is precipitated with ammonia. The precipitate is washed with water to get rid of the adhering ammonium oxalate. The process is repeated. The precipitate may be still further purified by precipitating its acid solution with ammonia.

The constitution of adrenaline

The chemical make-up of adrenaline, as well as its ultimate synthesis, became known as the result of the labors of several men; among whom may be mentioned von Fürth (23), Takamine (96), Jowett (50), Dakin (13), Pauli (62), Friedmann (21), Stoltz (85) and Flächer (16).

First of all we have Aldrich's formula, $C_9H_{13}O_3N$, which is the starting point. The ease with which adrenaline is oxidized and the green color obtained with ferric chloride suggests a catechol configuration. Takamine on potash fusion obtained protocatechuic acid

$$\begin{array}{c} \text{OH} \\ \text{OH} \\ \bigcirc \\ \text{COOH} \end{array}$$

suggesting the position of the third group in the molecule. Jowett confirmed and extended this observation by first methylating adrenaline and then oxidizing the product, giving him veratric acid

$$\begin{array}{c} \text{OCH}_3 \\ \text{OCH}_3 \\ \bigcirc \\ \text{COOH} \end{array}$$

and trimethylamine; suggesting, further, an —$NHCH_3$ grouping.   That methylamine can be split off was shown by von Fürth by heating adrenaline with aqueous alkali.   He also showed the presence of an alcoholic hydroxyl group.

The optical activity of adrenaline points to an asymmetric carbon atom in the side chain; which, in turn, leads to one of two possible formulas:

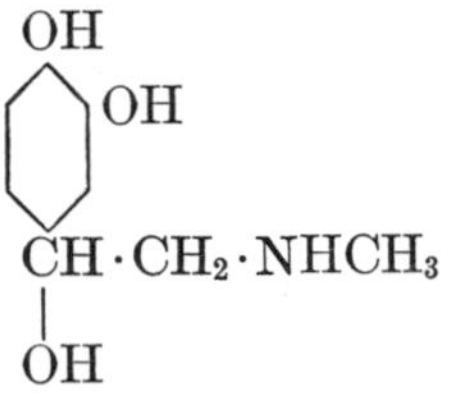

OH

OH

$CH \cdot CH_2 \cdot NHCH_3$

$\overset{|}{OH}$

I

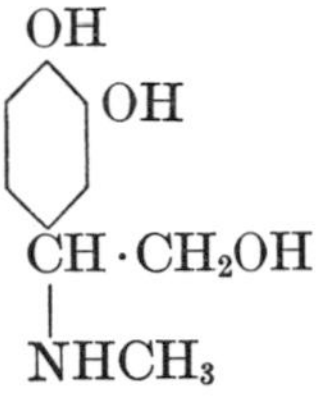

OH

OH

$CH \cdot CH_2OH$

$\overset{|}{NHCH_3}$

II

That adrenaline is a secondary alcohol, and therefore has the structure (I) was definitely proved by the synthesis of the compound; though Friedman's work had given indications of its structure.   He treated the hormone with benzene-sulfonyl chloride and obtained the tribenzene-sulfonyl compound (III), which on oxidation gave a ketone

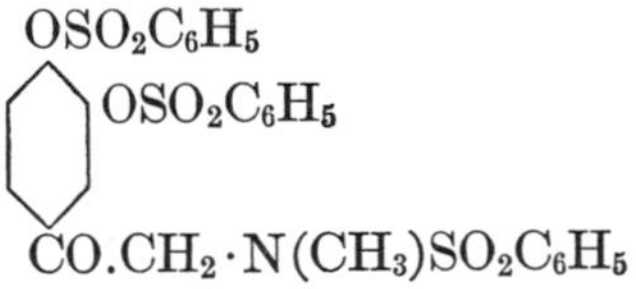

$OSO_2C_6H_5$

$OSO_2C_6H_5$

$CO.CH_2 \cdot N(CH_3)SO_2C_6H_5$

III

suggesting that adrenaline is a secondary alcohol.

Dakin and, more particularly, Stolz, are largely responsible for the actual synthesis of the compound.   Stolz did his work in the chemical laboratory of Meister, Lucius and Brüning, where the practical details necessary for commercial production were carefully worked out.

Catechol and chloracetylchloride (or a mixture of chloracetic acid and phosphorus oxychloride) are condensed to form chloracetocatechol:

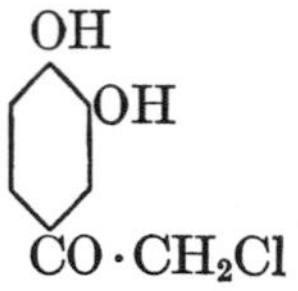

$$OH$$
$$OH$$
$$CO \cdot CH_2Cl$$

IV

Practical improvements in the preparation of this compound we owe to Mannich (55) and Ott (61). IV combines with a concentrated solution of methylamine in the cold to form the methylamino ketone:

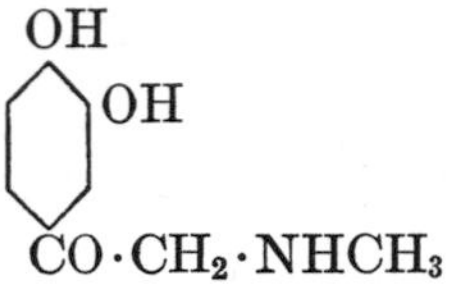

$$OH$$
$$OH$$
$$CO \cdot CH_2 \cdot NHCH_3$$

V

which on reduction (with aluminum amalgam or, still better, with hydrogen and palladium (5)) yields adrenaline.

However, the problem was not completely solved as yet; for the synthetic adrenaline, obtained as just described, is a racemic mixture and much less active, pharmacologically, than the product obtained from the adrenal glands, which is the *levo* compound. Flächer, another member of the firm of Lucius and Brüning, solved this problem by resolving the synthetic product. Flächer combined the *dl*-adrenaline with *d*-tartaric acid to form *dl*-adrenaline-*d*-tartaric acid. This compound was next treated with a minimum quantity of methyl alcohol. The *l*-adrenaline-*d*-tartrate remains insoluble, while the *d*-adrenaline-*d*-tartrate goes into solution.

Properties of adrenaline

Adrenaline is slightly soluble in cold, and more soluble in hot water; and—as has already been stated—can be precipitated from its solution by means of ammonia. The natural adrenaline, which is levorotatory $[(\alpha)_D = -53.3°)]$ is 15 times as active as the d-form. Being a base, it forms salts with acids, the hydrochloride being the common commercial product. It is insoluble in organic solvents. It dissolves in fixed alkalis but not in their carbonates or in ammonia (6). Its phenolic character, and the fact that it has two hydroxyl groups in the o-position, give rise to a number of color reactions. With ferric chloride, in neutral or weakly acid solution, a green color is obtained; the color changes to violet or red in the presence of alkali. Exposed to the air, the hormone turns brown—a change accelerated by oxidases, which produce black pigments resembling, some claim, the melanin of the skin. Sodium tungstate in phosphoric acid (Folin's reagent) gives rise to a blue color with adrenaline, and this has been used for quantitative determinations (17) (5). However, no chemical test distinguishes the two forms of adrenaline; and since the l- is physiologically the more important, a physiological assay, the pressor test, is made. This consists in comparing the effect on the blood pressure of an animal of a known (and standardized sample) with the unknown specimen (98). (The various chemical and physiological assays are discussed in detail by Munch (57).)

Clinical applications

The clinical applications of adrenaline, among them its action in constricting the blood vessels with consequent rise of blood pressure; its stimulation of the vagus center causing slowing of the heart; and its stimulating effect on the heart muscle; its vasoconstrictor action in hemorrhage; its effect in catarrhal and congestive conditions; etc.; are discussed in (58) (99) (49).

The precursor of adrenaline

The origin of adrenaline in the body—to what extent the hormone can be traced to tyrosine or its derivatives—is still

shrouded in some mystery. The question is discussed by
Barger (5). Recent work by Raper (48) has shed some
light on the question. Raper has shown 3:4-dihydroxy-
phenyl-alanine (*dopa*) to represent the first stage in the formation of melanin from tyrosine by the action of tyrosinase.
He has also shown that tyrosinase acts on 3:4-dihydroxy-
phenyl-*N*-methylalanine (*N*-methyldoppa) yielding a small
amount of pressor base, the activity of which increases on
reduction. He assumes that the pressor base is adrenalone,
the ketone form of adrenaline, and that adrenalone cannot
be oxidized by the enzyme.

Ephedrine

The fact that ephedrine is related chemically to adrenaline,
and, more important, the fact that the two, physiologically,
behave similarly, makes the inclusion of ephedrine desirable
in this chapter. Ephedrine has the formula

so that it is 1-phenyl-1-hydroxy-2-methylaminopropane. It
is obtained from *Ephedra vulgaris*, a Chinese plant, the stems
of which have been used medicinally by the Chinese for the
past 5,000 years. The four isomers of ephedrine (it contains
two asymmetric carbon atoms) have been prepared synthetically (58) (1) (20). A synthetic substitute for ephedrine has
also been suggested; it is α-phenyl-β-amino-ethanol sulfate,
$(C_6H_5 \cdot CHOH \cdot CH_2NH_2)_2 \cdot H_2SO_4$, a base closely related,
chemically, to adrenaline, ephedrine and tyramine (56a).

In this connection, the article by Hartung (47), in which
he discusses adrenaline and related compounds and the influence of structure on physiological activity, may be read with
profit.

THE CORTICAL HORMONE

That the cortex of the adrenals is more important to life than the medulla had long been known. Addison's disease, connected with a diseased cortex, could not be cured with adrenaline, which has its origin in the medulla. Important though adrenaline was shown to be, it was obviously not *the* hormone of the gland in the sense that thyroxine represents thyroid activity. All attempts to isolate a hormone other than adrenaline from the adrenal glands ended in failure until quite recently; and practically the entire part of this chapter deals with the amazing achievements during the last few years.

Stewart and Rogoff

In 1927 Stewart and Rogoff published a short paper dealing with the injection into adrenalectomized dogs of an adrenal extract made with 0.9 per cent salt solution and glycerine (73). "Until it has been shown," they write, "that any adrenal extracts whatever possess the power of definitely increasing the period of survival after removal of the adrenals, the assumption that the cortex produces a hormone (which might appropriately be called *interrenalin*) must lack a foundation. . . . " Using more than 100 control dogs, the survival period of the majority of these animals after double adrenalectomy was a week to 10 days. The longest survival period in the case of one dog was 16 days. Among the 30 dogs treated with extracts, one lived into the eighteenth day, one into the twentieth day, one into the twenty-second day, one into the twenty-third day, one into the twenty-eighth day, and one survived 78 days after removal of the second adrenal. That adrenaline, which was present to some extent in the extracts, might have this beneficial effect was ruled out completely, because the injection of adrenaline alone, in greater quantity than could have been contained in any dose of extract injected, gave no such result.

These results were confirmed and extended in subsequent papers (74) (75) (84) (83). A study of the survival period of untreated adrenalectomized cats was also made. The average survival period of 26 male cats was 11 days, and of 20 non-pregnant female cats, 10 days. This knowledge was important, because in most of the subsequent work, cats were the subjects, very largely because it is easier to remove the adrenals in the cat than in any of the other common laboratory animals except the rat (and a large proportion of white rats survive indefinitely the loss of both adrenal glands).[1] Stewart and Rogoff's rather impure extract was also used in a number of cases of Addison's disease, with some beneficial effect.

Swingle and Pfiffner

From 1930 on Swingle, Pfiffner and their co-workers have published papers in rapid succession giving details of active fractions which they have prepared. In one of their early papers (89) they record that the maximum limit of the life-span of control operated cats is 15 days, the average life-span being 7.7 days. Various preliminary trials suggested that a lipid fraction would be the most promising starting material. Subsequent work (90) led to the discovery that the lipid fraction (obtained by an alcohol-benzene extraction process) could be treated with acetone, into which passed the active material, leaving behind phospholipids; and that further purification was possible by selective distribution between 70 per cent alcohol and petroleum ether, the hormone passing into the former. The method of preparation is as follows: 10 pounds of beef adrenal glands (packed in ice, and collected at the slaughter house the previous day) have their fat and connective tissue removed, and the glands are split lengthwise and the medullary tissue scraped

---

[1] Very recent work (24), (28) tend to show that this is not true. Some survive and some succumb quickly. But wherever there is a survival, we have evidence that minute amounts of accessory tissue are still there.

out.[2] The cortical tissue weighs 3000 grams. It is ground,
mixed with 2.5 volumes of 95 per cent alcohol and allowed to
remain at room temperature, with occasional stirring, for
three days. The mixture is strained through muslin, the
tissue residue expressed in a press, and the strained fluid is
filtered. The gland residue is reground and extracted in a
similar manner for 3 days with 2 volumes (based on fresh
gland weight) of 80 per cent alcohol. The alcoholic extracts
are concentrated separately in partial *vacuo* at a temperature
of 50° to 60°C. to about one-fifteenth their original volume.
Each aqueous residue is mixed with an equal volume of
benzene and set aside in the refrigerator. (From this stage
on, all material is kept in the refrigerator, except when under
manipulation.) The benzene solution is removed and the
washings repeated until the last benzene washing is only
slightly yellow. The benzene washings are combined, and
the benzene removed in partial *vacuo* at a temperature of
45° to 50°C. The brown semi-solid lipid residue weighs
81.0 grams.

To this residue is added 500 cc. of acetone. The material
is thoroughly rubbed and set aside for 24 hours. The acetone solution is decanted and the residue is re-extracted.
After decanting the second acetone extractives, the residue
is transferred to a mortar and rubbed with five 100-cc. portions of acetone. The combined acetone extracts are removed *in vacuo* at 45° to 50°C. The residue weighs 14.7
grams.

This residue is transferred to a separatory funnel containing
30 cc. of petroleum ether (B.P. 30° or 40° to 60°) and 74
cc. of 95 per cent alcohol. 26 cc. of water are added
and the contents mixed. The 70 per cent alcohol layer is
washed 5 times with 30-cc. portions of petroleum ether.
The petroleum ether and washings are returned to the original

[2] We shall see presently that this is not necessary, and that a very efficient method is at our disposal for removing adrenaline in the extracts.

flask, the petroleum ether removed *in vacuo* at 40° to 50°C. and the distribution procedure repeated. The petroleum ether solution resulting from the second distribution is run into a separatory funnel, and 74 cc. of 95 per cent alcohol and 26 cc. of water are added. The petroleum ether solution resulting from the third distribution is treated similarly. The alcoholic solutions are washed with 30-cc. portions of petroleum ether. The inactive petroleum ether-soluble material weighs 13.2 grams. The 70 per cent active soluble material weighs 1.489 grams.

At this point, whatever adrenaline is present may be removed by passing the solution through permutit (64). The 70 per cent alcohol-soluble fraction, which contains 1.49 grams of solids, includes 36 mg. of adrenaline. The solvents are removed by distillation *in vacuo* at 45° to 50°C. The residue is taken up in 100 cc. of 95 per cent alcohol, and the solution is filtered through two 30-gram portions of permutit. The filtrate contains 0.41 gram of solids, including less than 1 mg. of adrenaline; it is concentrated to 100 cc., and the filtration procedure repeated, using two 15-gram portions of permutit. The filtrate contains 0.4 gram solids, including approximately 0.05 mg. of adrenaline. The alcoholic solution is concentrated to 100 and 70 cc. of distilled water is added. The alcohol is removed and the extract diluted to 100 cc. with water. The milky, watery suspension (containing the active material) is clarified and sterilized by passing through a Seitz filter. The filtered extract contains 0.29 gram of solids, including approximately 0.05 mg. of adrenaline. The pH is 5.65. Eight-tenths per cent sodium chloride is added to render the extract isotonic. One cubic centimeter represents 30 g. of fresh beef adrenal cortex. (See, also, (65) and (88).)

The use of permutit made it possible for Swingle and Pfiffner to prepare active extracts from whole beef adrenal glands, thereby doing away with the preliminary dissection

(91). The procedure just described is used, except that one starts with whole adrenal glands. A new method for removing adrenaline is also described in this paper. It consists in distributing an active fraction between aqueous alkali and an immiscible solvent such as benzene or ether. Adrenaline passes into solution in the aqueous alkali, whereas the cortical hormone is found in the immiscible solvent phase. In their more recent work the authors have abandoned this fractionating step, owing to losses.

Even in their earliest crude lipid fraction, Swingle and Pfiffner were able to show how very effective their extract was. The average life-span for controls (cats) was 7.7 days (38 animals),[3] and the average for the adrenalectomized cats treated with their extracts was 27.8 days (23 animals). None of the controls survived over 15 days, and none of the extract-treated animals survived less than 16 days. One cubic centimeter of extract (representing 30 grams of fresh cortical tissue) per kilo of body weight was the amount injected daily (89). In their next publication (90), in which an aqueous extract was used, but which still contained adrenaline, survival periods of extract treated animals up to, and beyond, 100 days are recorded. During this period, such animals behaved quite normally; and it was only when the extract was withdrawn that the animals broke down very rapidly, some of them dying within the first two weeks. The success in removing adrenaline from their potent fractions (64) made it possible for the authors to show that animals verging on death from adrenal insufficiency can be restored to a normal condition within 72 hours following the first intraperitoneal injection. Subcutaneous and intravenous injections may also be employed. With intravenous injections, it becomes necessary to remove the water-insoluble fraction after permutit purification with Seitz filtration (91).

[3] Later it was shown to be 8.6 (100 animals) (88).

Although the cortical hormone can be separated from adrenaline by means of dilute aqueous alkali, saponification destroys it. The hormone is also thermolabile. Extracts are rendered inactive by boiling in an open flask for two minutes. One-tenth per cent benzoic acid has proved to be an excellent preservative; in its presence, the hormone can be kept for comparatively long periods at room temperature (91).

The most potent (and purest) of these extracts gives a negative biuret, ninhydrin, Hopkins-Cole, Molisch, Pauli, Knoop and Lieberman-Burchard reaction. It gives a positive xanthoproteic, Millon's, alkaline copper and alkaline phosphotungstate reactions.

A striking symptom seen in the cat suffering from adrenal insufficiency is a marked drop in the rectal temperature. There is also a drop in the metabolic rate. These changes disappear after treatment with cortical hormone (65), (93). The changes in the respiratory exchange following bilateral adrenalectomy are the same, whether the thyroid is intact or totally removed (100). Swingle and Pfiffner, extending their experiments to dogs, have bred adrenalectomized animals on extract treatment and have obtained healthy pups, "some of which are alive and well 6 months after birth" (88). Normal dogs have been given huge quantities of the cortical hormone, with apparently no effect; in this respect the hormone behaves much like the hormone obtained from the anterior pituitary and the gonads, and very much unlike adrenaline, insulin, thyroxine and the parathyroid hormone.

There is definite evidence of renal failure in animals deprived of their adrenals. The kidney function is promptly restored following administration of the cortical hormone. A very early detectable change in an adrenalectomized dog is an elevation in non-protein nitrogen and urea. By using the N.P.N. and urea as a criterion, it is possible to determine the minimum dose of extract which will maintain operated dogs in normal health (88) (31).

A dog unit is defined by Harrop as the minimum daily dose of cortical hormone necessary to maintain normal physiological conditions in the adrenalectomized dog for a period of 7 to 10 days; the two criteria of normal physiological condition being maintenance of body weight and blood level of non-protein-nitrogen (or urea). Different batches of cortical hormone extract assay 4 to 10 dog units (D.U.) per cubic centimeter.

In a recent paper (66), Pfiffner, Swingle and their associates point out that extracts obtained by them from the whole gland are much more potent than those prepared from dissected cortex (on an equivalent weight basis).   Here is the comparison:

Whole gland		*Dissected cortex*
1000 grams	=	720 grams
57.5 mgm. active fraction		60 mgm. active fraction
25 cc. extract		24 cc. extract
40–80 D.U. per cubic centimeter		4–10 D.U. per cubic centimeter
Yield 1000 to 2000 D.U.		Yield 96 to 240 D.U.

They also record a somewhat simplified technique in preparing the hormone, yielding a potency equal to former preparations but containing less solid material.   In this method the glands are extracted once with alcohol for 48 hours, the benzene-soluble fraction is extracted twice with acetone, the acetone-soluble fraction is distributed twice between 70 per cent alcohol and petroleum ether, and the alcohol-soluble fraction is filtered only once through permutit.   Freezing the whole gland for 5 months prior to extraction does not effect the yield of hormone. "The glands may even be autolysed for 48 hours at room temperature and still prove the source of a good yield of hormone. (See, also, (67).)

The very amazing clinical application of the cortical hormone in Addison's disease we shall refer to later (see p. 138).

Hartman and his collaborators

As early as 1927 Hartman and his associates reported the preparation of an extract of the cortical hormone (to which Hartman proposed to give the name *cortin*) (44). The preliminary steps involved extraction with water (in the presence of a slight amount of acetic acid) and salting out with sodium chloride. An acidulated extract is saturated with sodium chloride. The hormone is in the precipitate. Eighty per cent alcohol dissolves the hormone and coagulates the protein. The alcoholic extract is evaporated and enough water is added to the residue to make an isotonic solution (41) (33).[4] The average survival days of adrenalectomized cats treated with this extract ran as high as 21. The daily injection of these extracts into completely adrenalectomized cats "simulated chronic adrenal insufficiency" (43).

Quite a different method, based on the solubilities of the hormone in fat solvents, was published two years later (33). Here the cortical material is extracted with ether. The ether in the ether extract is removed by distillation and the residue is extracted with 80 per cent alcohol, which takes up the hormone. The alcohol in the alcoholic extract is removed *in vacuo* and the residue is taken up with water (33).

As finally refined (40) (37), the fresh adrenal cortex is finely ground and extracted with peroxide-free ether. (The work should be done in a dark room or the flasks should be covered with an opaque cloth.) Four liters of ether should be used to 3 kg. of tissue. The air in the flask is replaced by carbon dioxide. The mixture should be agitated for 4 to 8 hours. After pouring off the ether extract, second and third extractions with ether are made. The combined ether extracts are concentrated almost to dryness *in vacuo*. The residue is extracted four times with 95 to 98 per cent alco-

---

[4] See, in this connection, the work of Goldzieher (25), who prepared an extract (called *interrenin* by him) by extracting the adrenals with N 2 HCl and precipitation with NaCl.

hol heated from 45° to 50°C.   For every kilo of gland tissue
50 to 60 cc. of alcohol are used in each extraction.   The
fractions are combined, enough water is added to make the
alcohol content 80 per cent; the solution is chilled to −10°C.
and filtered cold.   The filtrate is evaporated *in vacuo* and
the residue again extracted with a small volume of 60 to 75
per cent alcohol, then chilled and filtered as above.   The
alcohol is again removed and the residue extracted with a
small volume of ether.   "The ether is driven off and its
residue taken up with sufficient water to make the desired
concentration."   Sodium chloride is added to make the extract isotonic with the body fluids.   After passing through
a Seitz filter, the extract is ready for injection.   With this
extract, operated cats had been kept alive practically indefinitely.

Cortin, writes Hartman, lowers the blood urea when high,
increases the resistance to infection and cold and speeds
the repair of injury.   It proved ineffective by mouth.

For biological assay, Hartman suggests the use of young
rats (50 to 150 grams) who fail to gain weight, or even lose,
after removal of both adrenals.   The injection of sufficient
cortin enables these animals to grow and develop normally
(45).   With this assay method as a basis, some properties
of the hormone were investigated (39).   Antioxidants, such
as hydroquinone, resorcinol or levulose, retard the loss of
potency in aqueous solution.   The hormone can be preserved in 80 to 95 per cent alcohol for weeks; but it is destroyed by N 10 sodium hydroxide at 20°C. in less than one
hour.   On the other hand, N 10 ammonium hydroxide,
under the same conditions, has little or no effect.   Attempts
to extract the cortical hormone from the whole adrenals have
been but partially successful, due to the difficulty of separating cortin from the toxic substances which develop in the
medulla (but compare this with the work of Swingle and
Pfiffner, p. 127).   Active charcoal seems to remove both

cortin and toxic substances from an aqueous solution (pH 6.5 to 8). Permutit removes toxic substances and some cortin from an alcohol solution (but refer to Swingle's permutit method for removing adrenaline from the cortical hormone, p. 127). The same is true of Lloyd's reagent and of aluminum hydroxide.

Hartman has used still another test for biological assay: the ability of cortical extracts to protect adrenalectomized rats against cold (38). Normal rats show a fall in colonic temperature of a little more than 1°C. when exposed to cold (4° to 18°C.) for several hours. Cortin-treated adrenalectomized rats show a drop of 2° to 3°C.; while the isotonic sodium chloride-treated adrenalectomized rats show a fall of 12°C. or more, and many die. Injected adrenaline hydrochloride does not increase the resistance of adrenalectomized rats. The metabolism of the rats is also lowered 10 to 20 per cent by adrenalectomy but returns to normal when enough cortical hormone is injected.

(It may be noted, in passing, that Hartman's method for preparing the cortical hormone has been used by Perla and Marmorston-Gottesman to obtain an extract from ox spleen which protects adult male rats against *Bartonella muris* anemia following splenectomy; and it is suggested that the spleen extract contains a specific hormonal substance (63a).)

Several methods of preparing extracts containing the cortical hormone

The methods of Swingle and Pfiffner (p. 125) and Hartman p. 131) have already been given. A method by Rogoff will be found on page 138. Zwemer and his co-authors (103) (102) also employ an alcoholic extract, but they differ with others in certain, perhaps important, practical details. Beef adrenals, obtained from the slaughter house immediately after the kill and shipped in ice, have their connective tissue and fat dissected off and the glands are ground in a meat chopper. The minced glands are mixed with 95 per cent alcohol, in the proportion of one liter of alcohol per kilogram of gland, and allowed to stand in the cold overnight. The alcoholic extract is poured off and filtered first through coarse cheese cloth and then through coarse filter paper. The filter is washed with fresh alcohol, and the alcoholic filtrate and washings are saved (A). The adrenals (residue) are now extracted with alcohol in a continuous extraction apparatus for 84 hours under reduced pressure, and at a temperature of 35° to 40°C. This alcoholic extract is now combined with (A), and the mixture is allowed to remain in the cold for 12 hours. The white precipitate which forms is filtered off and discarded, and the filtrate is concentrated to one-half its volume under reduced pressure and again filtered. The precipitate is discarded, and the alcohol in the filtrate is removed under reduced pressure. The aqueous residue is allowed to stand in the cold for 24 hours and then centrifuged in ice at a speed of 2,000 R.P.M. for 10 minutes. A brown precipitate settles out and a few drops of orange-colored oil appear on the surface of the supernatant fluid. The supernatant fluid is withdrawn with a pipette and its equivalent in grams of gland computed. For sterilization, it is passed through a Seitz filter.

Further purification may be accomplished by shaking the supernatant fluid with an equal quantity of benzene. The benzene layer is removed, a small quantity of water added, and the benzene removed by evaporation under reduced pressure. The aqueous residue is extracted with ether. The ether fraction is shaken up with distilled water and the ether then removed by reduced pressure. The aqueous residue, which is the potent extract, is diluted with water when needed for injection. Tested with the Folin-Denis phenol reagent, it is free from adrenaline.

Zwemer finds that even normal animals react to his cortical extract, and he uses them for assays (104). The injection of 0.5 cc. per kilogram of body weight of an extract in which 1 cc. = 0.5 gram of fresh whole beef adrenal, will produce a rise in carbon dioxide-capacity and blood sugar. A fall occurs in the N.P.N. nitrogen, if it is high, and a rise, if it is normal. The same shift is found in the blood chlorides. Similar results have been obtained using cats, dogs and rabbits. The use of normal animals for tests, if efficient, will obviate the necessity for many adrenalectomies and also conserve material, "since we and others have found that it requires huge quantities of extract to keep adrenalectomized cats alive."

In experimental adrenal insufficiency, there is a fall in carbon dioxide-capacity, a rise in N.P.N., a fall in blood chlorides and a fall in blood sugar (104). The injection of the cortical extract causes the CO_2 and chlorides and the sugar to rise to normal and the N.P.N. fails to rise.

In preparing the cortical hormone, Kutz, in Collip's laboratory, has modified—and simplified, to some extent— the Swingle and Pfiffner's procedure (52). Beef whole glands are extracted with an equal volume of acetone. The acetone extract is concentrated at low temperature and pressure to one-thirtieth of its original volume. The concentrate is extracted 5 times with benzene. The combined benzene extracts are reduced in volume at low temperature and pressure and subsequently washed with 4 per cent sodium bicarbonate solution until all the adrenaline is removed. After further concentration, the benzene extract is converted into a watery extract by adding an equal volume of water to the benzene solution and removing the benzene by distillation. Acetic acid is added to the watery extract until maximum precipitation of lipoid is obtained. The precipitate is filtered off and discarded and the volume of the filtrate is so adjusted that 1 cc. represents 15 grams of whole gland.

It was discovered that immature rats in Collip's laboratory (Wistar strain), which had been inbred for a number of years, do not survive adrenalectomy, except in rare instances; and that injection of the hormone prolongs their lives. Kutz suggests that the rat unit be taken as the minimum daily dose of extract which will protect, for at least 20 days, 50 percent of a group of animals adrenalectomized at 28 days of age, the extract being administered subcutaneously twice daily.

One of the most recent methods for preparing the cortical hormone has been suggested by Grollman and Firor (28). They, like Kutz, use acetone as their extracting medium, rather than alcohol (Swingle and Pfiffner) or ether (Hartman), thereby getting relatively small quantities of fatty material in their extract.   They find the use of sodium bicarbonate for the extraction of the adrenaline more efficient than filtration through permutit.   Swingle and Pfiffner's distribution of the hormone between aqueous alcohol and petroleum ether is also avoided.   The preliminary freezing of the glands is important in order to get maximum yields of hormone.   The method is as follows: The beef glands (whole glands, or glands from which the medulla is removed), are cleaned from fat and connective tissue, cut into small pieces and dropped into a freezing mixture consisting of acetone cooled almost to its freezing point by the addition of lumps of solid carbon dioxide. (The freezing mixture stops enzymatic processes which destroy the active principle.)   The frozen tissue is ground and mixed with acetone in the proportion of 1 kg. of adrenal cortex and 3 volumes of technical acetone.   The mixture is allowed to remain in the ice-chest overnight and then pressed in a wine-press, yielding filtrate (A).   The residue is again placed in the ice-chest with sufficient acetone to cover it and is then heated on a water bath at 65°C. for 20 minutes and then pressed out, yielding filtrate (B).   The combined filtrates, (A) and (B), are reduced *in vacuo* at 25° to 30° to 1300 cc. and filtered through gauze after cooling. The aqueous filtrate is now extracted 7 times with 180-cc.

portions of benzene. The combined benzene solutions are chilled and shaken twice with 65-cc. portions of cold, saturated sodium bicarbonate. The benzene solution is now shaken with 10 cc. of N hydrochloric acid, to neutralize any excess alkali, and the benzene solution is evaporated *in vacuo* at 35° to 40°C. During the distillation 100 cc. (less if more concentrated extracts are desired) of 0.9 per cent saline are added dropwise. The solution is cooled and filtered through a sterile Seitz filter.

The extract, if made up in distilled water, contains less than 1 mg. of total solids per cubic centimeter. The potency of the extract is tested on adrenalectomized 1-month-old rats. With adequate therapy there is normal growth, as evidenced by a daily increase in weight of several grams. The animals should finally be allowed to die of insufficiency, which occurs unless the original operation is incomplete. The average amount of extract necessary to permit normal growth in a 40- to 50-gram rat when given in a daily intra-peritoneal injection is defined as a rat unit.

A preliminary announcement of Kendall (51) emphasizes the importance of extracting the gland with acetone in the presence of sulfuric acid (to pH of about 3), otherwise only a small percentage of the active material is obtained. After concentrating the acetone solution to a small volume, the adrenaline, ascorbic acid, lactic acid, etc., are removed with lead acetate and sodium bicarbonate in the presence of methyl alcohol and acetone. From the fraction soluble in acetone the last traces of adrenaline are removed with solid lead nitrate and anhydrous potassium carbonate.

Britton, who has criticized the work of Stewart and Rogoff and Hartman (at least, Hartman's earlier work), because the former give few details of their method of extraction and the latter's directions are somewhat confusing (7), reports complete success with extracts prepared by the Swingle and Pfiffner method (9) (10), even when administered orally (in the proportion, however, of 3 to 5 times the intraperitoneal dose) (8).   He is of the opinion that "adrenal insufficiency may perhaps be considered in synonymity with glycogen insufficiency" (11).   Adrenalectomized cats suffer severe derangement in carbohydrate metabolism.   The glucose in the blood and the glycogen in the liver are greatly reduced, the latter sometimes almost to the vanishing point. Muscle glycogen is greatly diminished while the lactates are increased.   "The carbohydrate changes are revolutionary enough in themselves to bring about death of the animal. The administration of cortical hormone causes a complete reversal of these disordered conditions."   These views have not gone unchallenged.

Addison's disease

While we have no intention in this book to discuss clinical applications, the recent remarkable results obtained with the use of the cortical hormone in Addison's disease deserve some comment even in these pages.   The symptoms associated with disease of the adrenal glands (the cortex, more particularly, as we understand it today) were described by Thomas Addison in 1855 as "anemia, general languor and debility, remarkable feebleness of the heart's action, irritability of the stomach, and a peculiar change of color of the skin" (71) (76).

Stewart and Rogoff, in a series of publications (70) (72), claim to have obtained beneficial results by oral administration of their *interrenalin*, the cortical hormone.   "The comparison of cases treated with interrenalin and those under other treatment demonstrated decided prolongation of life and amelioration of symptoms in the former.   Permanent relief or cure of the syndrome, however, can rarely be accomplished" (72).   The rather incomplete information which these authors have given regarding the method of preparation of their interrenalin is somewhat offset by the following, which we find in one of Rogoff's latest papers (72), and which represents the method after a number of previous changes: Using sheep or cattle, the cortex is separated from the medulla, and the former is macerated with 2 volumes of physiological salt solution, to which is added a volume of glycerine equal to about one-fifth of the quantity of adrenal cortex used. The mixture is allowed to stand in the cold overnight, 10 volumes of 95 per cent alcohol are added, and the mixture is allowed to stand for 48 hours, with frequent shaking. The mixture is strained and the residue is again extracted with a mixture of 10 per cent alcohol and 5 per cent glycerine in physiological salt solution. The alcohol is removed *in vacuo* from the combined filtrates. "The product is now subjected to two or three extractions with petroleum benzin or benzene. To the aqueous portion is added a sufficient quantity of physiological solution of sodium chloride to make a final product corresponding to 1 gram cortex = 10 cc. extract. . . . For oral administration to human beings . . . a larger amount of glycerine is added in the original extraction; the aqueous solvent is reduced in quantity and in the process of removal of the alcohol, and it is not aimed to remove all the alcohol. Finally, the product is completed by the addition of glycerine, instead of physiologic solution of sodium chloride, to make the desired volume. This preparation is stable for many weeks if kept in a cool, dark place and in well-stoppered containers."

More convincing results have been obtained by Hartman and his co-workers (35) (34) (46) (42), whose extracts, from all one can judge, were probably more potent than those of Rogoff. Even in their study of their first subject suffering from Addison's disease (35), they could show that the subject had been kept alive for 5 months by the injection of cortical extract (some 5 cc. every 6 hours, 1 cc. representing 15 grams of cortex[5]). "Four relapses have occurred following reduction of extract. A few hours after increasing the

[5] Later an extract was prepared wherein 1 cc. contained the equivalent of 40 grams of cortex (42).

extract after a relapse, improvement was evident each time, and in two or three days recovery was almost complete. The appetite returned and mental activity became normal." The patient finally died of pneumonia 238 days after his first admission to the hospital. A pathological examination showed that the adrenal cortices were almost completely absent while the medullae were almost normal (34). Subsequent experience with some 20 patients has fully confirmed the beneficial effect of their extract (42).

Remarkable cases of recovery have been reported by Rowntree and his associates, using Swingle and Pfiffner's preparation. In the first recorded case, published late in 1930 (78), a patient with Addison's disease, and in a state of complete collapse, was given daily doses of 20 cc. subcutaneously (1 cc. being the equivalent of 30 grams of fresh beef cortex). "Within 36 hours a marked effect on appetite and strength was apparent. The patient, who had been so nauseated as to retain water with difficulty, now asked for wieners and sauerkraut and in lieu of the latter ate a double order of beef-steak with relish." The patient relapsed when a further supply of the extract was not available, but promptly recovered when a fresh supply became available. When extracts free from adrenaline became available, the material could be injected intravenously, with practically no local irritation.

In the following year, some 20 cases had been treated by Rowntree and Greene and the results in 15 were excellent (76).[6] "In our experience the cortical hormone of Swingle and Pfiffner is a specific remedy in the treatment of Addison's disease and the most potent preparation we have used. In most cases the immediate response is prompt and striking. The effect on hunger, the ingestion and retention of food and

[6] A course of treatment has usually consisted of from 40 to 60 cc. of the extract over a period of from 4 to 10 days (77).

the increase in weight and strength are impressive. However, the remedy is not invariably helpful. Cases have been observed of moderately advanced Addison's disease in which the results were lacking. . . . As a rule, the immediate effects in the crisis of Addison's disease are as striking as the effects of insulin in the acidosis and coma of diabetes mellitus. However, Addison's disease is a chronic condition caused, as a rule, by tuberculosis. Hence substitution treatment constitutes only one of these problems; usually tuberculosis must also be dealt with." (See, also, (79) (77) (80) (97) (32).)

The chemical and metabolic changes in Addison's disease are not very striking (26). The basal metabolic rate is usually slightly reduced. Gastric achlorhydria is common, creatinuria is sometimes present and the level of fasting blood sugar is slightly reduced. If the patient is losing weight the nitrogen balance is negative. These changes may partly be due to the poor nutritive condition of the patient.

The cortical hormone in the urine

Perla and Gottesman, using as their standard the quantity of cortex administered on the fifth and sixth day after suprarenalectomy necessary to protect the rats against 200 mg. of histamine per kilogram, obtained as active extract from urine (63). The urine of young male and female adults is extracted with benzene. The benzene fractions are evaporated at 40° *in vacuo* to dryness. The residue is taken up in ether, the ether evaporated off *in vacuo* and the residue taken up in water or oil. The final aqueous product contains no adrenaline and it is non-irritating when injected subcutaneously or intraperitoneally. It is made up so that 1 cc. of the extract is equivalent to 300 cc. of urine. The resistance to histamine of these rats is such that the authors estimate that one liter of urine furnishes an equivalent amount of protective substance to about ½ pound of whole gland. The female sex hormone of Doisy and the male hormone of Funk and Harrow (hormones also present in the urine) fail to raise the resistance of suprarenalectomized rats.

Grollman and Firor, utilizing as their standard the prolongation of life and the growth in one-month-old adrenalectomized rats (see p. 137), have prepared a urinary extract as follows (27): Fresh urine is extracted with benzene. The benzene extract is washed with water, the benzene is removed *in vacuo* at 40°C. and an amount of 0.9 per cent saline is added so that 1 cc. of the final extract corresponds to 1 liter of urine. One liter of urine, according to these authors, contains an amount of hormone corresponding to approximately only 0.5 gram of glandular tissue. Theelin, antuitrin and follutein (representing sex hormones in the urine) were ineffective in prolonging the life of adrenalectomized rats.

More than one hormone?

Schmitz and Kuhnau (81) argue for the presence of three active substances in the adrenal cortex: a cholesterol-lowering substance (B), a substance which lowers the amount of phosphatids (C) and another which raises this amount (A). Acetone extracts of the cortex from beef adrenals contains (A) and (B). An alcoholic extract of the dried residue from the acetone extraction contains (B) and (C). (A) and (B) are separated by dilution of the acetone solution with water, extraction with ether, evaporation, dilution with alcohol, saponification with sodium alcoholate, extraction of the unsaponified material with petroleum ether, evaporation and extraction with boiling methyl alcohol. (A) has the formula $C_{25}H_{40}O_3$; it contains one OH group and one double bond. (B) has the formula $C_{25}H_{36}O_3$ and also contains one OH group and one double bond. (C) has not yet been analyzed. The cholesterol-lowering substance (B) is said to be identical with the cortical hormone prepared by the Swingle and Pfiffner method. (This paper is so recent, that it is too early to pass judgment upon the results.)

The functions of the adrenal glands

(See, also, p. 129.)   Whilst it is no more our purpose to
discuss the functions of the glands than to discuss their
clinical importance, recent work in this direction has led to
important chemical results (the discovery of ascorbic acid).
"The fundamental significance of the adrenal cortex is unknown; practically all investigators agree upon this point"
(92).   Swingle and his co-workers have recently advanced
the hypothesis that the symptoms of adrenal insufficiency
and of traumatic or secondary shock are perhaps both due
to the failure of the blood volume and blood-diluting regula-
tor mechanism, the adrenal cortex (92).   The function of the
adrenal cortical hormone, according to them, is the regulation and maintenance of a normal circulating volume of fluid
within the vascular system.   In the absence of the hormone,
fluid is continually lost from circulation; and accompanying
the progressive decrease in blood volume there is a progressive fall of blood pressure to the death level.   Freeman, in a
critical analysis of Swingle's paper (19), points out that there
is, to begin with, one marked discrepancy between adrenal
insufficiency and traumatic shock, namely, that in the former
the blood sugar is low whereas in traumatic shock it is normal or elevated.   It is possible, as Britton points out (p. 138)
that death from adrenal insufficiency may result primarily
from the alterations in carbohydrate metabolism (which, in
turn, may exert some influence on blood hydration).   "Since
it is known that the deficiency of the cortico-adrenal hormone
results in a lowering of the glycogen and blood glucose levels;
and since it is known that if the blood glucose level is reduced by insulin, there is a reduction in blood volume with
blood concentration; the suggestion that the function of the
adrenal cortex is the regulation of blood volume and blood
dilution seems unnecessary."

Loeb has noticed a low concentration of sodium in the
blood serum of patients suffering from Addison's disease and

he has observed a patient with Addison's disease who recovered rapidly when sodium chloride was ministered (53).
This author believes that the regulation of sodium metabolism is one important function of the adrenal glands (53a) (30).

Szent-Györgyi has isolated from the adrenal cortex a
strong reducing substance (to which he originally gave the
name *hexuronic acid*, but which is now known as *ascorbic
acid*) identical with a substance obtained from various plant
sources. That this substance may be connected with the
absence of pigment in Addison's disease is suggested (94). In
the meantime, very laborious work in several laboratories has
apparently confirmed Szent-Györgyi's original contention:
that ascorbic acid and vitamin C are one and the same substance (87). Significantly enough, ascorbic acid disappears
from the adrenal glands of animals on a vitamin C-free diet
(82). This acid, with the formula $C_6H_8O_6$, has the structure

$$CH_2OH \cdot CHOH \cdot CH \cdot COH:COH \cdot CO$$
$$\underbrace{\qquad\qquad}_{O}$$

according to Hawarth, Hirst and co-workers (48a), (4a).
See also (95) and (68).[7]

A lactation hormone of the adrenal cortex

Hartman and his co-workers find that extracts prepared
according to their method, which removes fatty substances
by chilling to $-12°C.$, does not enable adrenalectomized
rats to supply milk; yet these extracts are potent so far as
the cortical hormone is concerned. If, however, the chilling is
not carried below $3°C.$, the extracts support lactation. "The
material chilled out between $3°C.$ and $-12C°.$ contains a sub-

---

[7] In the belief that ascorbic acid is
$$CH_2(OH)CH \cdot CH(OH) \cdot C(OH):C \cdot COOH,$$
$$\underbrace{\qquad\qquad}_{O}$$

Reichstein and co-workers have synthesized *d*-ascorbic acid by treating
d-xylonose with hydrogen cyanide and hydrolyzing the product with
hydrochloric acid (68).

stance necessary for milk production; since if an extract of this material is added to cortin and injected into adrenalectomized mother rats, they raise a much larger proportion of their young." The name *cortilactin* is suggested for this new hormone (12).

The presence of choline in cortico-adrenal extract

Eagle points out that considerable quantities of a highly undesirable impurity, choline, may be found in extracts prepared by the Swingle and Pfiffner method (p. 125),[8] though the extracts prepared according to the directions of Grollman and Firor (p. 136) are free from this base. Eagle is of the opinion that some of the properties attributed to the cortical extract (such as the influence on carbohydrate and respiratory metabolism) may be due to the presence of choline (14).

REFERENCES

(1) ABEL, J. J.: Chemistry in relation to medicine, with especial reference to insulin and other hormones. *Science*, **66**, 340 (1897).

(2) ABEL, J. J.: On a simple method of preparing epinephrine and its compounds. *Johns Hopkins Hosp. Bul.*, **13**, 29 (1902).

(3) ALDRICH, T. B.: A preliminary report on the active principle of the suprarenal glands. *Am. J. Physiol.*, **5**, 457 (1901).

(4) ALDRICH, T. B.: Adrenalin, the active principle of the suprarenal glands. *J. Am. Chem. Soc.*, **27**, 1074 (1905).

(4a) AULT, R. G., BAIRD, D. K., CARRINGTON, H. C., HAWARTH, W. N., HERBERT, R. W., HIRST, E. L., PERCIVAL, E. G. V., SMITH, F., AND STACEY, M.: Synthesis of *d*- and of *l*-ascorbic acid and of analogous substances. *J. Chem. Soc.*, Oct. (1933), p. 1419.

(5) BARGER, G.: Some Applications of Organic Chemistry to Biology and Medicine. (McGraw-Hill, New York. 1930.)

(6) BECKWITH, C. P.: The pharmacy of adrenalin. *J. Am. Pharm. Assoc.*, **3**, 1547 (1914).

(7) BRITTON, S. W.: Adrenal insufficiency and related considerations. *Physiol. Rev.*, **10**, 617 (1930).

(8) BRITTON, S. W., FLIPPIN, J. C., AND SILVETTE, H.: The oral administration of cortico-adrenal extract. *Am. J. Physiol.*, **99**, 44 (1931).

---

[8] This is denied by Swingle and Pfiffner.

(9) BRITTON, S. W., AND SILVETTE, H.: The cortical-adrenal hormone. *Science*, **73**, 322 (1931).

(10) BRITTON, S. W., AND SILVETTE, H.: Some observations on the cortico-adrenal hormone. *Science*, **73**, 373 (1931).

(11) BRITTON, S. W., AND SILVETTE, H.: The apparent prepotent function of the adrenal glands. *Science*, **75**, 644 (1932).

(12) BROWNELL, K. A., LOCKWOOD, J. E., AND HARTMAN, F. A.: A lactation hormone of the adrenal cortex. *Proc. Soc. Exp. Biol. and Med.*, **30**, 783 (1933).

(13) DAKIN, H. D.: The synthesis of a substance allied to adrenalin. *Proc. Roy. Soc.*, **B76**, 491, 498 (1905).

(14) EAGLE, E.: Presence and significance of choline in cortico-adrenal extract. *Proc. Soc. Exp. Biol. and Med.*, **30**, 1094 (1933).

(15) FIROR, W. M., AND GROLLMAN, A.: Studies on the adrenal. I. Adrenalectomy in mammals with particular reference to the white rat (*Mus norvegicus*). *Am. J. Physiol.*, **103**, 686 (1933).

(16) FLÄCHER, F.: Ueber die Spaltung des synthetischen *dl*-Suprarenins in seine optisch aktiven Komponenten. *Zt. physiol. Chem.*, **58**, 189 (1908); also D.R.P. 222,451.

(17) FOLIN, O., CANNON, W. B., AND DENIS, W.: A new colorimetric method for the determination of epinephrine. *J. Biol. Chem.*, **13**, 477 (1912).

(18) FOURNEAU, E.: Organic Medicaments and Their Preparation (Blakiston, Philadelphia. 1925).

(19) FREEMAN, N. E.: Cortin and traumatic shock. *Science*, **77**, 211 (1933).

(20) FREUDENBERG, K., SCHOEFFEL, E., AND BRAUN, E.: Study on the configuration of ephedrine. *J. Am. Chem. Soc.*, **54**, 234 (1932).

(21) FRIEDMANN, E.: Die Konstitution des Adrenalins. *Hofmeister's Beitrage chem. Physiol. Path.*, **8**, 95 (1906).

(22) FUNK, C., DUBIN, H. E., AND FREEDMAN, L.: Suprarenin (synthetic ephinephrine). *J. A. Ph. A.*, **12**, 952 (1923).

(23) FÜRTH, VON, O.: Zur Kenntnis der Brenz-katechinähnlichen substanz in der nebennieren. *Zt. physiol. Chem.*, **24**, 142 (1897).

(24) GAUNT, R.: Survival period of bilaterally adrenalectomised rats. *Proc. Soc. Exp. Biol. and Med.*, **29**, 823 (1932).

(25) GOLDZIEHER, M.: Interrenin, das Hormon der Nebennierenrinde. *Klin. Woch.*, **7**, 1124 (1928).

(26) GREENE, C. H., ROWNTREE, L. G., SWINGLE, W. W., AND PFIFFNER, J. J.: Metabolic studies in Addison's disease. *Am. J. Med. Sciences*, **183**, 1 (1932).

(27) GROLLMAN, A., AND FIROR, W. M.: Studies on the adrenal. II. Extraction of cortical hormone from urine. *Proc. Soc. Exp. Biol. and Med.*, **30**, 669 (1933).

(28) GROLLMAN, A., AND FIROR, W. M.: Studies on the adrenal. III. The preparation of an active extract of the hormone of the adrenal cortex. *J. Biol. Chem.*, **100**, 429 (1933).

(29) HARRIS, L. J., AND RAY, S. N.: Vitamin C and the suprarenal cortex. II. Loss of potency of guinea-pig suprarenal in scurvy. With notes on a method of determining antiscorbutic activity (hexuronic acid) by chemical means. *Biochem. J.*, **27**, 303 (1933).

(30) HARROP, G. A.: Diagnosis and treatment of Addison's disease. *J. Am. Med. Assoc.*, **101**, 388 (1933).

(31) HARROP, G. A., PFIFFNER, J. J., WEINSTEIN, A., AND SWINGLE, W. W.: A biological method of assay of the adrenal cortical hormone. *Proc. Soc. Exp. Biol. and Med.*, **29**, 449 (1932).

(31a) HARROP, G. A., SOFFER, L. J., ELLSWORTH, R., AND TRESCHER, J. H.: Studies on the suprarenal cortex. III. Plasma electrolytes and electrolyte excretion during suprarenal insufficiency in the dog. *J. Exp. Med.*, **58**, 17 (1933).

(32) HARROP, G. A., AND WEINSTEIN, A.: Addison's disease treated with suprarenal cortical hormone. *J. Am. Med. Assoc.*, **98**, 1525 (1932).

(33) HARTMAN, F. A.: Cortin, vital hormone of the adrenal cortex. *Endocrinology*, **14**, 229 (1930).

(34) HARTMAN, F. A., AND AARON, A. H.: Cortin in Addison's disease. *Endocrinology*, **16**, 43 (1932).

(35) HARTMAN, F. A., AARON, A. H., AND CULP, J. E.: The use of cortin in Addison's disease. *Endocrinology*, **14**, 438 (1930).

(36) HARTMAN, F. A., AND BROWNELL, K. A.: A further study of the hormone of the adrenal cortex. *Am. J. Physiol.*, **93**, 655 (1930).

(37) HARTMAN, F. A., AND BROWNELL, K. A.: The preparation of adrenal cortex. *Science*, **73**, 620 (1931).

(38) HARTMAN, F. A., BROWNELL, K. A., AND CROSBY, A. A.: The relation of cortin to the maintenance of body temperature. *Am. J. Physiol.* **98**, 674 (1931).

(39) HARTMAN, F. A., BROWNELL, K. A., AND CROSBY, A. A.: Certain factors in the preparation of cortin. *Proc. Soc. Exp. Biol. and Med.*, **28**, 962 (1931).

(40) HARTMAN, F. A., BROWNELL, K. A., AND HARTMAN, W. E.: A further study of the hormone of the adrenal cortex. *Am. J. Physiol.*, **95**, 670 (1930).

(41) HARTMAN, F. A., BROWNELL, K. A., HARTMAN, W. E., DEAN, G. A., AND MACARTHUR, C. G.: The hormone of the adrenal cortex. *Am. J. Physiol.*, **86**, 353 (1928).

(42) HARTMAN, F. A., GREENE, C. W., BOWEN, B. D., AND THORN, G. W.: Further experience with cortin therapy. *J. Am. Med. Assoc.*, **99**, 1478 (1932).

(43) HARTMAN, F. A., GRIFFITH, JR., F. R., AND HARTMAN, W. E.: Observations upon adrenalectomized cats treated with the cortical hormone. *Am. J. Physiol.*, **86**, 360 (1928).

(44) HARTMAN, F. A., MacARTHUR, C. G., AND HARTMAN, W. E.: A substance which prolongs the life of adrenalectomised cats. *Proc. Soc. Exp. Biol. and Med.*, **25**, 69 (1927).

(45) HARTMAN, F. A., AND THORN, G. W.: A biological method for the assay of cortin. *Proc. Soc. Exp. Biol. and Med.*, **28**, 94 (1930).

(46) HARTMAN, F. A., THORN, G. W., LOCKIE, L. M., GREENE, C. W., AND BOWEN, B. D.: Treatment of Addison's disease with an extract of suprarenal cortex (cortin). *J. Am. Med. Assoc.*, **98**, 788 (1932).

(47) HARTUNG, W. H.: Epinephrine and related compounds: Influence of structure on physiological activity. *Chem. Rev.*, **9**, 389 (1931).

(48) HEARD, R. D. H., AND RAPER, H. S.: A study of the oxidation of 3:4-dihydroxyphenyl-*N*-methylalanine with reference to its possible function as a precursor of adrenaline. *Biochem. J.*, **27**, 36 (1933).

(48a) HERBERT, R. W., HIRST, E. L., PERCIVAL, E. G. V., REYNOLDS, R. J. W., AND SMITH, F.: The constitution of ascorbic acid. *J. Chem. Soc.*, Sept. (1933), p. 1270.

(49) HUNT, R., McCANN, W. S., ROWNTREE, L. G., VOEGTLIN, C., AND EGGLESTON, C.: The intravenous use of glandular products. *J. Am. Med. Assoc.*, **92**, 2099 (1929).

(50) JOWETT, H. A. D.: Constitution of epinephrine. *J. Chem. Soc.*, **85**, 192 (1904).

(51) KENDALL, E. C., MASON, H. L., McKENZIE, B. F., AND MYERS, C. S.: The physiological action and the chemical nature of the active principle in the suprarenal gland essential to life. *Proc. Am. Soc. Biol. Chem.*, **8**, 59 (1933).

(52) KUTZ, R. L.: A method of assay of extracts containing the suprarenal cortical hormone. *Proc. Soc. Exp. Biol. and Med.*, **29**, 91 (1931).

(53) LOEB, R. F.: Effect of sodium chloride in treatment of a patient with Addison's disease. *Proc. Soc. Exp. Biol. and Med.*, **30**, 808 (1933).

(53a) LOEB, R. F., ATCHLEY, D. W., BENEDICT, E. M., AND LELAND, J.: Electrolyte balance studies in adrenalectomized dogs with particular reference to the excretion of sodium. *J. Exp. Med.*, **57**, 775 (1933).

(54) MAGISTRIS, H.: Ueber die Biochemie der Nebennierenrinde, I. Darstellung und Nachweis des Hormon der Nebennierenrinde. *Biochem. Zt.*, **248**, 39 (1932).

(55) MANNICH, C., AND HAHN, F. L.: Ueber eine Synthese von α-Aminoketonen mittels Hexamethylenetetramin. *Ber.*, **44**, 1548 (1911).

(56) MAY, PERCY: The Chemistry of Synthetic Drugs (Longmans, New York. 1921).

(56a) MILLER, H., AND PINESS, G.: A synthetic substitute for ephedrine. *J. Am. Med. Assoc.*, **91**, 1033 (1928).

(57) MUNCH, J. C.: Bioassays (Williams & Wilkins, Baltimore. 1931).

(58) New and non-official remedies, 1933. (*Amer. Med. Assoc.*, Chicago.)

(59) OLIVER, G., AND SCHÄFER, E. A.: On the physiological action of extracts of the suprarenal capsules. *J. Physiol.*, **16**, 1 (1894).

(60) OLIVER, G., AND SCHÄFER, E. A.: The physiological effects of extracts of the suprarenal capsules. *J. Physiol.*, **18**, 230 (1895).

(61) OTT, E.: Zur Kenntnis der Adrenalin-Synthese. *Ber.*, **59B**, 1068 (1926).

(62) PAULY, H.: Zur Kenntniss des Adrenalins. *Ber.*, **36**, 2944 (1903).

(63) PERLA, D., AND MARMORSTON-GOTTESMAN, J.: A substance in urine of normal human adults that raises the resistance of suprarenalectomized rats. *Proc. Soc. Exp. Biol. and Med.*, **28**, 1024 (1931).

(63a) PERLA, D., AND MARMORSTON-GOTTESMAN, J.: Studies on *Bartonella muris* anemia. VI. A lipoid extract of the spleen that prevents *Bartonella muris* anemia in splenectomized albino rats. *J. Exp. Med.*, **56**, 777 (1932).

(64) PFIFFNER, J. J., AND SWINGLE, W. W.: Studies on the adrenal cortex. III. The revival of cats prostrate with adrenal insufficiency with an aqueous extract of the cortex. *Am. J. Physiol.*, **96**, 180 (1931).

(65) PFIFFNER, J. J., AND SWINGLE, W. W.: The preparation of adrenal cortical hormone. *Endocrinology*, **15**, 335 (1931).

(66) PFIFFNER, J. J., VARS, H. M., BOTT, P. A., AND SWINGLE, W. W.: A quantitative study of adrenal cortical hormone extraction. *Proc. Soc. Exp. Biol. and Med.*, **29**, 998 (1932).

(67) PFIFFNER, J. J., VARS, H. M., BOTT, P. A., AND SWINGLE, W. W.: Further purification of the adrenal cortical hormone. *Proc. Soc. Exp. Biol. and Med.*, **29**, 1267 (1932).

(68) REICHSTEIN, T., GRUSSNER, A., AND OPPENAUER, R.: Die Synthese der *d*-Ascorbinsaure (*d*-Form des C-Vitamins). *Helv. Chim. Acta*, **16**, 561 (1933).

(69) RICHARDSON, E. P.: The surgical application of epinephrin. *J. Am. Med. Assoc.*, **83**, 1587 (1924).

(70) ROGOFF, J. M.: Clinical and experimental studies on adrenal insufficiency and Addison's disease and the treatment of such conditions by interrenalin. *Proc. California Acad. Med.*, 1930.

(71) ROGOFF, J. M.: Diagnosis and treatment of Addison's disease. *Canadian Med. J.*, **24**, 43 (1931).

(72) ROGOFF, J. M.: Addison's disease. Further report on treatment with "interrenalin" (adrenal cortical extract). *J. Am. Med. Assoc.*, **99**, 1309 (1932).

(73) ROGOFF, J. M., AND STEWART, G. N.: The influence of adrenal extracts on the survival period of adrenalectomized dogs. *Science*, **66**, 327 (1927).

(74) ROGOFF, J. M., AND STEWART, G. N.: Suprarenal cortical extracts in suprarenal insufficiency (Addison's disease). *J. Am. Med. Assoc.*, **92**, 1569 (1929).

(75) ROGOFF, J. M., AND STEWART, G. N.: Studies on adrenal insufficiency. VIII. The survival period of untreated adrenalectomised cats. *Am. J. Physiol.*, **88**, 162 (1929).

(75a) ROWNTREE, L. G., AND BALL, R. G.: Diseases of the suprarenal glands. *Endocrinology*, **17**, 263 (1933).

(76) ROWNTREE, L. G., GREENE, C. H., BALL, R. G., SWINGLE, W. W., AND PFIFFNER, J. J.: Results of treatment with cortical hormone of the suprarenal gland. *Trans. Assoc. Am. Physicians*, **46**, 123 (1931).

(77) ROWNTREE, L. G., GREENE, C. H., BALL, R. G., SWINGLE, W. W., AND PFIFFNER, J. J.: Treatment of Addison's disease with the cortical hormone of the suprarenal gland. *J. Am. Med. Assoc.*, **97**, 1446 (1931).

(78) ROWNTREE, L. G., GREENE, C. H., SWINGLE, W. W., AND PFIFFNER, J. J.: The treatment of patients with Addison's disease with the "cortical hormone" of Swingle and Pfiffner. *Science*, **72**, 482 (1930).

(79) ROWNTREE, L. G., GREENE, C. H., SWINGLE, W. W., AND PFIFFNER, J. J.: Addison's disease. Experiences in treatment with various suprarenal preparations. *J. Am. Med. Assoc.*, **96**, 231 (1931).

(80) ROWNTREE, L. G., AND SNELL, A. M.: Addison's Disease. (W. B. Saunders Co., Philadelphia. 1931.)

(81) SCHMITZ, E., AND KUHNAU, J.: Über die innere Sekretion der Nebennierenrinde. *Biochem. Zt.*, **259**, 301 (1933).

(82) SIEHRS, A. E., AND MILLER, C. O.: Disappearances of vitamin C from adrenals of guinea-pigs having scurvy. *Proc. Soc. Exp. Biol. and Med.*, **30**, 696 (1933).

(83) STEWART, G. N.: The adrenal glands. *Archives Int. Med.*, **43**, 733 (1929).

(84) STEWART, G. N., AND ROGOFF, J. M.: Studies on adrenal insufficiency. IX. The influence of extracts of adrenal cortex (sheep and cattle) on the survival period of adrenalectomised dogs and cats. *Am. J. Physiol.*, **91**, 254 (1929).

(85) STOLZ, F.: Ueber Adrenalin und Alkylaminoacetobrenzcatechin. *Ber.*, **37**, 4149 (1904); also D. R. P. 152,814 and English patent 1903, 25,480.

(86) SVIRBELY, J. L., AND SZENT-GYÖRGYI: Function of the adrenal medulla. *Nature*, **129**, 541 (1932).

(87) SVIRBELY, J. L., AND SZENT-GYÖRGYI, A.: The chemical nature of vitamin C. *Biochem. J.*, **27**, 279 (1933).

(88) SWINGLE, W. W.: The cortical hormone of the adrenal gland. *Harvey Lectures*, 1931–32. (Williams & Wilkins, Baltimore.)

(89) SWINGLE, W. W., AND PFIFFNER, J. J.: Studies on the adrenal cortex. I. The effect of a lipid fraction upon the life-span of adrenalectomised cats. *Am. J. Physiol.*, **96**, 153 (1931).

(90) SWINGLE, W. W., AND PFIFFNER, J. J.: Studies on the adrenal cortex. II. An aqueous extract of the adrenal cortex which maintains the life of bilaterally adrenalectomised cats. *Am. J. Physiol.*, **96**, 164 (1931).

(91) SWINGLE, W. W., AND PFIFFNER, J. J.: Studies on the adrenal cortex. IV. Further observations on the preparation and chemical properties of the cortical hormone. *Am. J. Physiol.*, **98**, 144 (1931).

(92) SWINGLE, W. W., PFIFFNER, J. J., VARS, H. M., BOTT, P. A., AND PARKINS, W. M.: The function of the adrenal cortical hormone and the cause of death from adrenal insufficiency. *Science*, **77**, 58 (1933).

(93) SWINGLE, W. W., PFIFFNER, J. J., AND WEBSTER, B.: Effect of adrenal cortical hormone upon respiratory metabolism of adrenalectomised cats. *Proc. Soc. Exp. Biol. and Med.*, **28**, 728 (1931).

(94) SZENT-GYÖRGYI, A.: On the mechanism of biological oxidation and the function of the suprarenal gland. *Science*, **72**, 125 (1930).

(95) SZENT-GYÖRGYI, A.: Identification of vitamin C. *Nature*, **131**, 225 (1933).

(96) TAKAMINE, J.: Adrenalin, the active principle of the suprarenal glands and its mode of preparation. *Amer. J. Pharm.*, **73**, 523 (1901).

(97) THOMPSON, J. T., AND WHITEHEAD, R. W.: Some clinical results from the use of adreno-cortical extract as prepared by the method of Swingle and Pfiffner. *Endocrinology*, **15**, 495 (1931).

(98) U. S. Pharmacopoeia, 10th Ed. 1926.

(99) WEARN, J. T.: Pharmacology of epinephrin. *J. Am. Med. Assoc.*, **83**, 1508 (1924).

(100) WEBSTER, B., PFIFFNER, J. J., AND SWINGLE, W. W.: Effect of adrenal cortical hormone upon respiratory metabolism of normal, thyroidectomized and thyroidectomized-adrenalectomized cats. *Proc. Soc. Exp. Biol. and Med.*, **28**, 1021 (1931).

(101) WEBSTER, B., PFIFFNER, J. J., AND SWINGLE, W. W.: The effect of the adrenal cortical hormone upon the respiratory metabolism of the cat. *Am. J. Physiol.*, **99**, 710 (1932).

(102) ZWEMER, R. L.: An adrenal cortex extract: its development and experimental and clinical use. *Endocrinology*, **15**, 382 (1931).

(103) ZWEMER, R. L., AGATE, JR., F. J., AND SCHROEDER, H. A.: A method for preparing an active adrenal cortex extract. *Proc. Soc. Exp. Biol. and Med.*, **28**, 721 (1931).

(104) ZWEMER, R. L., AND SULLIVAN, R. C.: A blood-chemical test for adrenal cortex extracts. *Proc. Soc. Exp. Biol. and Med.*, **28**, 723 (1931).

CHAPTER VI

THE MALE HORMONE

Within the last few years several investigators have succeeded in obtaining an extract which controls the secondary
sexual characters in the male—"internal, such as the accessory reproductive organs, and external, such as some horn
growth and the growth of the cock's comb" (43). So much
is definite, but beyond this we cannot go, unless we are willing to enter the region where fact and fancy blend into one
another. Nor are we in a position to draw any definite conclusions at this stage as to the availability of this hormone
for clinical purposes. That it may have some uses in treating
human beings has been suggested (1) (37); but it is too early
to pass final judgment. The tendency at present is to regard
this hormone as but one of several factors which play their
part in the regulation of the normal reproductive process.
Undoubtedly, the anterior (sex) pituitary must be considered
as one other factor to be reckoned with (see, for example,
(16) (21a) (50)).

As late as 1927 an author reviewing the subject wrote:
"Die Bemühungen zur Darstellung des Hormons, welches
dem männlichen Organismus die sekundaren Geschlechtsmerkmale verleiht, sind bis jetzt kaum weiter gediehen als
zur Zeit Brown-Séquards." The situation seemed little
clearer to authors two years later (52). The Brown-Séquard
mentioned here published a paper in 1889 in which he recorded the extraordinary effects on himself upon the injection
of watery extracts of dog and guinea-pig testes (21). These
results have not been substantiated. But it must be ad-
mitted that, beginning with Berthold in 1849 and ending

with Steinach in our own day, a number of earnest workers paved the way for the more positive results of recent work.[1]

The many conflicting results and the many failures are at once understandable when we remember that for a long time no dependable test method was at hand. This difficulty was overcome with Pézard's discovery that the capon could be used as a test object. He claimed that the injection of the equivalent of "one-tenth of a cryptorchid hog testis" caused an increase in size of the comb and wattles of the capon. The lack of details in his paper makes it well-nigh impossible to repeat and confirm his claims. But one thing remains certain: the comb growth in capons can be used as a test object, as the Chicago group (McGee, Koch, Moore, Gallagher), Funk and Harrow, and others have recently shown.

TEST METHODS

While the capon test is the one which finds most favor at present, and apparently the one which more nearly approaches the stage of yielding dependable quantitative data, other tests are also available. We owe to Moore more than to any other the careful study of these various "indicator methods," among which are the spermatozoön motility test (guinea pig) (44) (29) (40) (41); the electric ejaculation test (guinea pig) (44); the prostrate cytology test (rat) (44) (51); the seminal vesicle test (rat) (44) (48) (53) (33) (55) (5) (16) (29)[2] (29a); the vas deferens (rat) (53); and the Cowper's gland (rat and guinea pig) (22). A fish test, based upon the nuptual coloration of the bitterling, has also been proposed (20b). For those interested in these various tests the original papers must be consulted. We shall confine ourselves to the comb growth test in the capon.

[1] For a review of the earlier literature see (21) and (27).

[2] The accelerating effects in seminal vesicle growth when both the male hormone and an anterior pituitary-like substance are injected may be noted (16), (21a).

In many of our own experiments (18), the cocks were castrated when they were two months old. The method of
measurement consisted in measuring the distance from the
highest point to the base line, the vertical line being measured
at right angles to the base line. We confined ourselves, in
other words, to height measurements. Koch and his co-
workers take into consideration both the length and the
height of the comb. They measure the total length of the
blade from the anterior end to the posterior tip, and the
height is obtained by measuring one selected point, such as
the barble most directly under the eye. The product of the
length by the height (LH) is taken as an expression of comb
size (40). Dodds and his co-workers measure merely the
length of the comb (5). Freud (8) (9) favors a planimetric
method of measurement; the combs are laid upon photo-
graphic paper and exposed to light for a short time; after
which the surface of the comb is determined by planimetric
measurement of the silhouette. (See, also, (51a).) A potent extract from the testes or from urine will cause a rapid
comb growth in from 4 to 5 days and a very marked improvement in the general appearance of the bird. At the end of
four weeks or so the treated and control birds are not easily
distinguished. Should the injections be stopped, the head
furnishings regress; and in 4 to 6 weeks the capon resembles
the bird before treatment. Depending upon the method of
preparation, the daily injection of extracts obtained from 50
to 100 grams of testicular tissue or from 75 to 250 cc. of male
urine is needed to produce the desired effects.

The "cock unit" which we adopted (18) is the amount of
male hormone which, when injected, will increase the size of
comb and wattlers to the extent of 10 mm. in 10 days. For
each test six animals are used and the average taken. Koch
and Gallagher (28) define their bird unit as the amount
of hormone which, when injected intramuscularly for five
days, causes an average of 5 mm. in the sum of the increase

in length and height of the comb of at least five brown leghorn capons. Comparative studies with different "indicator methods" have led Moore and Gallagher (46) to reach the following conclusions: the minimal effective dose for the spermatozoan motility test is approximately 0.07 bird unit (as defined by Koch and Gallagher); for the prostrate test, 0.10 bird unit; for the seminal vesicle, Cowper's gland, and vas deferens test, 0.40 bird unit; and for the electric ejaculation test, 1 to 1.5 bird units. The minimal effective dose on the bird in five days is 0.5 to 0.7 bird unit. The "rat unit" or the amount of active substance required to maintain the normal condition in castrated rats when injected daily for a twenty-day period, is 6 bird units.

SOURCES

Active extracts have been prepared from mammal testes (bull, boar, ram, goat), from male urine, from the blood of males, from the testicle of fetal calves, from the urine of pregnant and non-pregnant women and from the blossoms of the pussy willow (43) (57) (58). The most convenient source is undoubtedly urine. But it has been shown that the male hormone is practically absent in the urine of boys under ten years of age and present in very small quantities in the urine of men of sixty and above (12) (17) (18) (56) (27) (58).

METHODS OF PREPARATION

For the time being we shall confine ourselves to methods which yield active preparations in sufficient purity so that they can be injected without any toxic effects.

FROM TESTES

We select the method of Koch and his co-workers (20) (19) (27). The testes, after being freed from epididymides and tunics, are finely hashed and extracted for three or four days at room temperature with from 3 to 4 volumes of 95 per cent alcohol. The alcoholic solution obtained is concentrated under diminished pressure until an aqueous emulsion or suspension of lipins is obtained. This is then repeatedly shaken with equal volumes of benzene and the combined benzene extracts evaporated under diminished pressure. The resulting lipin mixture is next dissolved in acetone and cooled to 10°C. The clear acetone solution is separated from the inert precipitate and again evaporated under diminished pressure. This can not be taken up with ether, the ether evaporated and the residue dissolved in olive oil. The material is ready for injection. If a purer product is desired, the acetone-soluble material may be treated as follows:

In a particular experiment, 36 grams of the acetone-soluble material, obtained as just outlined, was next dissolved in 175 cc. of hexane and shaken with 125 cc. of 70 per cent alcohol. The 70 per cent alcohol layer was washed five times with hexane. The total hexane-soluble material was then re-extracted twice with 75 cc. of 70 per cent alcohol, and in each case the alcohol layer was washed five times with fresh hexane. The 70 per cent alcohol-soluble material after removal of the alcohol was transferred to ether and shaken with 10 cc. of 10 per cent sodium hydroxide. The sodium hydroxide solution was washed five times with fresh portions of ether and the ether solution shaken repeatedly with water. The ether-soluble material is finally taken, the ether removed and the residue dissolved in olive oil.

Various modifications of this procedure may be found in the following papers: (6) (5) (10); though it should be stated that in none of them are the descriptions so detailed and so explicit as in the articles by Koch and his collaborators.

FROM URINE

It is, of course, possible to apply the same principles to the extraction of the male hormone from urine (see, for example,

(58)). However, the following method, which we elaborated (15) (14) (18) is simple and efficient: The urine (which may be collected and stored in bottles containing enough hydrochloric acid to prevent alkaline fermentation) is acidified to congo red, if necessary, then strongly acidified (40 cc. of concentrated hydrochloric acid per liter of urine) and extracted with chloroform under reflux for 8 hours, using the temperature of the steam bath. Two liters of chloroform are used for every ten liters of urine. The product is cooled and most of the upper (watery) layer is carefully poured off. The residue is transferred to a separatory funnel, stirred and allowed to stand for a little while. The chloroform layer is now drawn off. The emulsion in-between the chloroform layer and the residual urine is next drawn off, filtered through several fluted filters and washed with a little chloroform. The filtrate is again separated in a separatory funnel, the chloroform fraction drawn off and added to the main chloroform portion. The chloroform extracts are evaporated, first by distillation on a water bath, and finally by distillation *in vacuo*, to remove the last traces of the solvent. The residue is next heated under reflux with sodium hydroxide for two hours. (For 30 liters of urine we use 10 grams of sodium hydroxide dissolved in 50 cc. of water.) The residue is extracted repeatedly (six to eight times) with ether, the ether evaporated, and the final residue taken up in oil.

Modifications of this procedure may be found in the following papers: (5) (35) (10) (24); but again it must be confessed that the lack of details in them is somewhat disconcerting. (See, however, the recent article by Gallagher and Koch (20a).)

It should be stated that administering the extract by mouth, even in ten-fold doses, produces little, if any effect (18) (27). The best results are obtained by subcutaneous or intramuscular injections.

PROPERTIES

Like the female hormone, the male hormone is soluble in fat solvents (ether, chloroform, acetone, benzene, etc.); and indeed, up to a certain point, the method of extraction of the two hormones may be quite similar. However—and this principle can be used for separation of the two—after saponification with sodium hydroxide the male hormone can be extracted with ether, whereas in the case of the female hormone it is necessary first to acidify the saponified material and then to extract with ether (14) (4). Whereas the female hormone shows acidic characteristics, the male hormone is neutral in reaction, being insoluble in alkali. The hormone is relatively heat-stable (for example, little destruction occurs by sterilizing the extract at 15 pounds pressure and 110°C.), and resistant to the action of acids and alkalis in moderate concentrations. It is very difficultly soluble in water. Pepsin and trypsin destroy the active factor (5). A benzene solution of the male hormone can be washed with strong acids and alkalis, and the active substance can be extracted from a 50 per cent alcohol-water solution with light petroleum. After such purification and careful drying, the hormone can be distilled in high vacuum (see, also, (20)).

THE CHEMICAL COMPOSITION OF THE HORMONE

A recent publication by Butenandt (3) leads to the belief that this talented chemist has actually isolated the male hormone in a chemically pure form. Unfortunately, at the time of writing no experimental details of the work are available beyond the substance of an address. But from it we may gather the following information: Using the capon as the test animal and Freud's planimetric method of measurement (8) (9), Butenandt first obtained active extracts from the urine by employing the Funk and Harrow procedure. The next step, somewhat vague in the description, will best be given in Butenandt's words: "Dieses Röhol liefert nach wiederholter Hydrolyse eine gereinigte Neutralfraction, aus der sich durch Entmischen mit organischen Lösungsmitteln und wässrigen alkohol eine alkohollösliche Charge abtrennen lässt." In the hope that the male hormone might show structural relationships to the female hormone, various hydroxyl and keto reagents were tried; and it was found that a crystalline product could be obtained with hydroxylamine which was highly active when recrystallized from dilute alcohol and injected into capons. The melting point of the colorless oxime proved to be 215°C. The oxime was next decomposed with dilute acid, and from the decomposition product a substance, recrystallized from dilute alcohol and with a melting point of 165°C., was obtained. Further purification became possible by fractional sublimation of the decomposition product using very high vacuum ($\frac{1}{10,000}$ mm. Hg.). The fraction distilling from 80° to 85° was collected, repeatedly recrystallized from dilute alcohol, and again sublimed, using high vacuum. The final product had a melting point of 178°C. and proved far more active than any hitherto known extract. Twenty-five thousand liters of male urine were needed to get 15 mgm. of the crystalline hormone.

The hormone contained no nitrogen, and an elementary analysis led to the formula $C_{16}H_{26}O_2$. An analysis of the oxime gave the formula $C_{16}H_{27}O_2N$ (which is in agreement with the reaction $C_{15}H_{26}O.CO + H_2 NOH$). Butenandt has published a later paper on the chemistry of the sex hormones (3B) in which the formula $C_{19}H_{30}O_2$ for the male hormone is advanced (3a).

In addition to the one keto group which the hormone molecule contains, its reaction to acetic anhydride reveals one hydroxyl group; and its failure to absorb bromine suggests a saturated compound. The important point is brought out that whereas the hydroxyl group present in the female hormone molecule is acidic in reaction (phenolic?), the similar group present in the male hormone molecule is neutral. That a chemical relationship exists between the male and the female hormone is postulated by Butenandt. (See, also, (52a).)

(The German patents (576,713 (May 15, 1933)) and 578,040, June 9, 1933, describe the preparation of derivatives of the male hormone based on its ketonic structure. See also Brit. 392,434, May 18, 1933. Phthalic anhydride condenses with the male hormone to form the phthalic acid ester (Germ. 584,211, Sept. 16, 1933), (Brit. 391, 686, May 4, 1933). Acylating agents also give derivatives (Germ. 576,967, May 19, 1933).)

MORE THAN ONE MALE HORMONE?

McCullagh (36) advances the view that there are at least two hormones generated by the testes, a water-soluble as well as a fat-soluble hormone. Whereas the later will cause regeneration of the atrophic secondary sex glands of castrated rats, but will neither prevent nor correct the hypertrophy of the pituitary gland and adrenals after castration, aqueous testicular extracts prevent the cellular changes from appearing in the pituitary gland after castration of rats and inhibit the hyperfunction of the pituitary gland.

REFERENCES

(1) BENJAMIN, H.: The male hormone. *Med. J. Record*, June 4 (1930).

(2) BLYTH, J. S. S., DODDS, E. C., AND GALLIMORE, E. J.: Observations on the assay of the comb-growth promoting hormone. *J. Physiol.*, **73**, 136 (1931).

(3) BUTENANDT, A.: Über die chemische Untersuchung der Sexualhormone. *Zt. angew. Chem.*, **44**, 905 (1931).

(3a) BUTENANDT, A.: Ueber die Chemie der Sexualhormone. *Zt. angew. Chem.*, **45**, 655 (1932).

(3b) BUTENANDT, A.: Zur Biologie und Chemie der Sexualhormone. *Naturwissenschaften*, **21**, 49 (1933).

(4) DINGEMANSE, E., FREUD, J., KOBER, S., LAQUEUR, E., LUCHS, A., AND MUNCH, A. W. P.: Zur Trennung des männlichen (Sexual-) Hormons von weiblichen (Menhormon). *Biochem. Zt.*, **231**, 1 (1931).

(5) Dodds, E. C., Greenwood, A. W., Allan, H., and Gallimore, E. J.: Properties of the comb-growth promoting substance obtained from testes and urine. *Biochem. J.*, **24**, 1031 (1930).

(6) Dodds, E. C., Greenwood, A. W., and Gallimore, E. J.: Note on a water-soluble active principle isolated from the mammalian testes and urine, and its relation to estrin. *Lancet*, p. 683 (1930).

(7) Fremery, P. de, Freud, J., and Laqueur, E.: Zur Messmethode von mannlichem Hormon. *Pflüger's Archiv f. ges. Physiol.*, **226**, 740 (1930).

(8) Freud, J.: On the biological tests of the male hormone. *Proc. Second Inter. Congress for Sex Research*, p. 304 (1930).

(9) Freud, J.: Über die männlichen Geschlechtsmerkmale der Leghorn-hühner, besonders über den Kamm, als Grundlage eines Testobjektes für die Eichung des männlichen Hormons. *Pflügers' Arch. ges. Physiol.*, **228**, 1 (1931).

(10) Freud, J., Jongh, S. E. de, Laqueur, E., and Munch, A. P. W.: Über männliches (sexual-) Hormon. *Klin. Wochschr.*, Nr. 17, p. 772 (1930).

(11) Freud, J., Jough, S. E. de, Laqueur, E., and Munch, A. P. W.: Über männliches (sexual-) Hormon. *Klin. Wochschr.*, Nr. 40, p. 1871 (1930).

(12) Funk, C., and Harrow, B.: The male hormone. *Proc. Soc. Exp. Biol. and Med.*, **26**, 325 (1929).

(13) Funk, C., and Harrow, B.: The male hormone. *Proc. Second Int. Congress for Sex Research*, p. 308 (1930).

(14) Funk, C., and Harrow, B.: The male hormone, IV. *Biochem. J.*, **24**, 1678 (1930).

(15) Funk, C., and Harrow, B.: The male hormone. *Proc. Am. Soc. Biol. Chem.*, **7**, 70 (1931).

(16) Funk, C., and Harrow, B.: The male hormone. V. Effect of the male hormone and the anterior pituitary. *Am. J. Physiol.*, **101**, 218 (1932).

(17) Funk, C., Harrow, B., and Lejwa, A.: The male hormone. II. *Proc Soc. Exp. Biol. and Med.*, **26**, 569 (1929).

(18) Funk, C., Harrow, B., and Lejwa, A.: The male hormone. *Am. J. Physiol.*, **92**, 440 (1930).

(19) Gallagher, T. F.: Distribution of testicular comb-growth stimulating principle in tissues. *Am. J. Physiol.*, **87**, 447 (1928).

(20) Gallagher, T. F., and Koch, F. C.: The testicular hormone. *J. Biol. Chem.*, **84**, 495 (1929).

(20a) Gallagher, T. F., and Koch, F. C.: Biochemical studies on the male hormone as obtained from urine. *Endocrinology*, **18**, 107 (1934).

(20b) Glaser, E., and Haempel, O.: Der Nachweis des männlichen Sexualhormons mit dem Fischtest. *Deutsche med. Woch.*, **58**, 1247 (1932).

(21) HARROW, B.: Glands in Health and Disease. (Dutton, New York. 1928.)

(21a) HARROW, B., NAIMAN, B., AND FUNK, C.: The male hormone. VI. Further experiments on the effect of the male hormone and the anterior pituitary. *J. Biol. Chem.*, **100**, lii (1933).

(22) HELLER, R. E.: Cowper's gland as a testis hormone indicator. *Proc. Soc. Exp. Biol. and Med.*, **27**, 751 (1930).

(23) JUHN, M., D'AMOUR, F., AND WOMACK, E. B.: The effects of simultaneous injections of the female and male hormones in capons. *Am. J. Physiol.*, **95**, 641 (1930).

(24) KABAK, J. M.: Männliches Geschlechtshormon aus dem Harn und seine Prüfung an Vogeln. *Endokrinologie*, **9**, 84 (1931).

(25) KABAK, J. M.: Männliches Geschlechtshormon aus dem Harn und Seine Prüfung an Saugetieren. *Endokrinologie*, **9**, 250 (1931).

(26) KABAK, J. M.: Männliches Geschlechtshormon aus Frauenurin. *Endokrinologie*, **10**, 12 (1932).

(27) KOCH, F. C.: The extraction, distribution and action of testicular hormones. *J. Am. Med. Assoc.*, **96**, 937 (1931).

(28) KOCH, F. C., AND GALLAGHER, T. F.: The testicular hormone. *J. Am. Med. Assoc.*, **98**, 738 (1932).

(29) KORENCHEVSKY, V.: The assay of testicular hormone preparations. *Biochem. J.*, **26**, 413 (1932).

(29a) KORENCHEVSKY, V., DENNISON, M., AND KOHN-SPEYER, A.: The rat unit of testicular hormone. *Biochem. J.*, **26**, 2097 (1932).

(30) LAQUEUR, E., FREMERY, P. DE, FREUD, J., JONGH, S. E. DE, KOBER, S., LUCHS, A., AND MUNCH, A. P.: Einheit oder Mehrheit männlicher Sexualhormone. *Ber. ges. Physiol.*, **61**, Nr. 3/4 (1931).

(31) LOEWE, S.: Das Hormon der männlichen Keimdruse (Androkinin). *Die Medizinische Welt*, Nr. 38 (1930).

(32) LOWE, S., VOSS, H. E., LANGE, F., AND WAHNER, A.: Sexualhormon in Männlichen Harn. *Klin. Woch.*, **7**, 1376 (1928).

(33) LOEWE, S., AND VOSS, H. E.: Gewinnung, Eigensehaften und Testierung eines männlichen Sexualhormons. *Akad. d. Wissenschaften in Wien*, Oct. 24, (1929).

(34) LOEWE, S., AND VOSS, H. E.: Der Stand der Erfassung des Männlichen Sexualhormons (Androkinins). *Klin. Woch.*, Nr. 11, p. 481 (1930).

(35) LOEWE, S., VOSS, H. E., ROTHSCHILD, F., AND BORCHARDT, E.: Uber den Nachweis männlichen Sexualhormons (Adrokinins) in Harne. *Biochem. Zt.*, **221**, 461 (1930).

(36) McCULLAGH, D. R.: Dual endocrine activity of the testes. *Science*, **76**, 19 (1932).

(37) McCULLAGH, E. P., McCULLAGH, D. R., AND KICKEN, N. F.: Diagnosis and treatment of hypogonadism in the male. *Endocrinology*, **17**, 49 (1933).

(38) McGEE, L. C.: The effect of the injection of a lipoid fraction of bull testicles in capons. *Proc. Inst. Medicine of Chicago*, April 22 (1927).

(39) McGee, L. C., Juhn, M., and Domm, L. V.: The development of
     secondary sex characters in capons by injection of extracts of bull
     testes. *Am. J. Physiol.*, **87**, 406 (1928).
(40) Moore, C. R.: On the properties of the gonads as controllers of
     somatic and psychical characteristics. *Biol. Bull.*, **55**, 339 (1928).
(41) Moore, C. R.: On the properties of the gonads as controllers of
     somatic and psychical characteristics. X. Spermatozoön activity
     and the testis hormone. *J. Exp. Zool.*, **50**, 455 (1928).
(42) Moore, C. R.: The physiologic effects of non-living testis grafts.
     J. Am. Med. Assoc., **94**, 1912 (1930).
(43) Moore, C. R.: The regulation of production and the function of the
     male sex hormone. *J. Am. Med. Assoc.*, **97**, 518 (1931).
(44) Moore, C. R., and Gallagher, T. F.: On the prevention of castra-
     tion effects in mammals by testis extract injection. *Am. J. Phys-
     iol.*, **89**, 388 (1929).
(45) Moore, C. R., and Gallagher, T. F.: Seminal-vesicle and prostate
     function as a testis-hormone indicator; the electric ejaculation
     test. *Am. J. Anat.*, **45**, 39 (1930).
(46) Moore, C. R., and Gallagher, T. F.: Threshold relationships of
     testis hormone indicators in mammals; the rat unit. *J. Phar-
     macol.*, **40**, 341 (1931).
(47) Moore, C. R., Gallagher, T. F., and Koch, F. C.: The effects of
     extracts of testis in correcting the castrated condition in the fowl
     and in the mammal. *Endocrinology*, **13**, 367 (1929).
(48) Moore, C. R., Hughes, W., and Gallagher, T. F.: Rat seminal-
     vesicle cytology as a testis-hormone indicator and the prevention
     of castration changes by testis-extract injection. *Am. J. Anat.*,
     45, 109 (1930).
(49) Moore, C. R., and McGee, L. C.: On the effects of injecting lipoid
     extracts of bull testes into castrated guinea pigs. *Am. J. Physiol.*,
     87, 436 (1928).
(50) Moore, C. R., and Price, D.: Some effects of fresh pituitary homo-
     implants and of the gonad-stimulating substance from human
     pregnancy urine on the reproductive tract of the male rat. *Am.
     J. Physiol.*, **99**, 197 (1931).
(51) Moore C. R., Price, D., and Gallagher, T. F.: Rat-prostate cy-
     tology as a testis thormone indicator and the prevention of castra-
     tion changes by testis-extract injections. *Am. J. Anat.*, **45**, 71
     (1930).
(51a) Ogata, A., and Ito, Y.: Untersuchung des männlichen Sexual-
     hormons. *J. Pharmaceut. Soc.* (Japan) **53**, 39 (1933).
(52) Trendelenberg, P.: Die Hormone. (Springer, Berlin. 1921.)
(52a) Tschering, K.: Zur Biochemie des testikelhormons. *Ergebnisse
     der Physiol.*, **35**, 301 (1933).
(53) Vatna, S.: Rat vas deferens cytology as a testis hormone indicator
     and the prevention of castration changes by testis extract injec-
     tion. *Biol. Bull.*, **58**, 322 (1930).

(54) Voss, H. E.: Zur Frage der Extra-hormonalen Beziehungen zwischen Gonaden und sekundaren Geschlechtsmermalen. *Arch. f. Entwicklungsmechanik der Organismen.* **122**, 584 (1930).

(55) Voss, H. E., AND Loewe, S.: Schnelltest auf mannliches Sexual hormon. *Deutche Med. Woch.*, Nr. 30 (1930).

(56) Womack, E. B., AND Koch, F. C.: Biochemical studies on the yield of testicular hormone from tissue and body fluids and on factors affecting the comb growth response in the brown leghorn capon. *Proc. Second Int. Congress for Sex Research*, p. 329 (1930).

(57) Womack, E. B., AND Koch, F. C.: Studies on the extraction of the testicular hormone from tissues and its quantitative distribution therein. *Endocrinology*, **16**, 267 (1932).

(58) Womack, E. B., AND Koch, F. C.: The testicular hormone content of human urine. *Endocrinology*, **16**, 273 (1932).

(59) Womack, E. B., Koch, F. C., Domm, L. V., AND Juhn, M.: Some factors affecting the comb growth response in the brown leghorn capons. *J. Pharmacol.*, **41**, 173 (1931).

CHAPTER VII

THE FEMALE HORMONES[1]

The publication by Allen and Doisy in 1923 recording the results with their "ovarian hormone" led at first to the belief that this hormone was the chief endocrine factor involved in the female sexual cycle. However, as this chapter and the one following will show, the corpus luteum and the anterior pituitary gland develop hormones which play their rôle in the sex activity of the female. In the meantime, we shall confine ourselves to Allen and Doisy's "ovarian hormone."[2]

Allen and Doisy succeeded where others failed primarily because they developed a test method based on the work of Stockard and Papanicolaou (96). "During the anabolic phase of the cycle (the estrual changes) the epithelium of the vagina grows to a considerable thickness and a cornified layer similar to that in the epidermis develops. During the catabolic phase, the outer layers of this epithelium degenerate and are removed by leucocytic action. These changes provide a definite succession of cell types in the vaginal lumen, each one characteristic of a certain phase of the cycle. Thus the microscopic examination of vaginal smears is a reliable indicator of the estrual condition of the living animal" (85). These cyclic phenomena in the genital tract cease entirely upon double ovariectomy. A potent extract should there-

---

[1] Many are the names which have been suggested for this hormone. Here are some of them: ovarian hormone; feminin; follicular hormone; folliculin; oestrin; menformon; amniotin; theelin; progynon; α-hormone; estrus-producing hormone; dioxyestrin; ketohydroxyestrin. The names "theelin" and "oestrin" have been widely adopted.

[2] References to earlier work will be found in (74) (42) (29) (45) (104) (91) (6).

fore produce the phenomena of estrus in the ovariectomized animal.

Allen and Doisy defined their rat unit as the minimum amount necessary to induce estrus with complete cornification of the vaginal mucosa as judged from a smear, in 75 per cent of a large group of ovariectomized sexually mature rats. The accepted rat unit (R.U.) is the highest dilution of the active material which, when given in three divided doses at four-hour intervals, will produce estrus (cornification and desquamation of the vaginal epithelium) in the castrated, mature rat, at the end of three days after the first injection. The effect must be obtained in four out of five animals (91). This "unit," as is now realized, is at best very approximate, for there are a number of factors which make for variability in results. The topic has been discussed at length ((84) (89) (24) (76) (12) (46) (45) (91) (38) (6)) and many suggestions for improving the test have been made. A simple modification, particularly applicable to clinical work, is given by Kurzrok (73).

At first Allen and Doisy used fresh liquor folliculi as their starting material. A convenient source at present is the urine of pregnant women (10) and the urine of pregnant mares (105); but the female hormone (which we shall call *theelin* from now on) can also be obtained from corpus luteum, the blood of pregnant and non-pregnant women, the urine of non-pregnant women, the placenta and the male blood and male urine (9) (48). The anterior pituitary-like hormone in the urine of pregnancy has been discussed in a previous chapter (p. 97).

The original Allen-Doisy method may be given first, since this work has paved the way for all subsequent improvements:

Fresh liquor folliculi is added to a double volume of 95 per cent alcohol and allowed to stand for 24 hours. The coagulum is filtered, the filtrate is distilled to remove the alcohol, and the residue is extracted with ether. The ether extract is evaporated and the solids are dried in a vacuum desiccator. The residue is dissolved in a small quantity of ether and a double volume of acetone is added. This solution and precipitation are repeated twice. The precipitates are discarded. The combined filtrates are evaporated and the residue is dried. This solid material is boiled with 95 per cent alcohol, filtered, the alcohol in the filtrate is evaporated off, and the residue taken up in purified corn oil (5). Improvements in the process were published later (94).

Theelin—a name coined by Doisy—is a substance soluble in fat solvents. Up to a certain point, it shows striking resemblances in its properties to the male hormone. This similarity in properties can very well be made use of in the preparation of active material. Assuming that the source is the urine of pregnant women, the material can be strongly acidified and extracted with chloroform in precisely the way described under "male hormone" (p. 157); with this exception: after refluxing with sodium hydroxide, the product is first made definitely acid before it is extracted with ether.[3]

A simple method, adapted for clinical use, is described by Kurzrok (13). The urine is made weakly acid with acetic acid, saturated with sodium chloride and extracted in a continuous extractor with ethyl acetate. The ethyl acetate extract is evaporated *in vacuo* and the residue is taken up in olive oil. Starting with 700 cc. of urine, one ends up with 10 cc. of active material (in olive oil). For the biologic assay, "two groups of castrated rats (3 animals in a group)

---

[3] To make the solution acid, it is best to saturate it with CO_2. While it is true that better yields are obtained if the solution is made acid before extracting with ether, it is possible, as Doisy points out, to extract the hormone with ether from alkaline solutions, even though the procedure is far from quantitative. Theelin shows weak acid properties.

are injected with the oil, subcutaneously, in the back, at 9
a.m. and 5 p.m. of the first day and 9 a.m. of the second day.
Group 1 receives 0.5 cc. of oil at each injection.   Group 2
receives 0.25 cc. of the oil at each injection.   Vaginal smears
are taken 48, 56 and 72 hours after the first injection.   The
vaginal secretion is spread in a drop of saline on a glass slide.
If no fewer than two animals of a group show the cornified
cells characteristic of estrus, the injected material may be
considered active.   Mucus, leucocytes and epithelial cells
must be absent to establish a positive result.   The least
amount of oil necessary to produce a positive smear is considered as containing one rat unit."

$$\frac{10}{y} \times \frac{1000}{700} = \text{rat unit per liter of urine,}$$

where y = total amount of oil injected into a single rat from
the group receiving the smallest amount ncessary to produce
positive smears.

Another simple method—which, incidentally, was used by
Marrian to show the presence of theelin in male urine (52)—
is as follows: The urine is preserved with toluol, evaporated
to a small bulk under reduced pressure, and the residue is
dried with anhydrous sodium sulfate.   The dried material
is extracted with ether in a Soxhlet apparatus, the ether extract is washed 4 to 6 times with water and evaporated to
dryness.   The residue is again treated with ether (5 to 10
cc.), filtered from small quantities of amorphous pigments,
the filtrate is evaporated to dryness, weighed and emulsified
in 1 to 2 cc. of 0.5 per cent Na_2CO_3.   A few drops of olive
oil are added to give smoother and more stable emulsions.

FEMALE SEX HORMONE IN BLOOD

Frank has shown the presence of an estrus-producing substance in the blood (59) (60).   Forty cubic centimeters of
blood is dried with anhydrous sodium sulfate and extracted

with ether.   The ether-soluble residue, taken up in 2 cc. of water, is injected in three equal portions at four-hour intervals into a previously castrated adult white mouse (61).

ISOLATION OF THE THEELIN AND THEELOL IN A CHEMICALLY PURE STATE

Four groups of workers in four different countries have been active in this field.   In America Doisy, in England Marrian, in Holland Dingemanse, and in Germany Butenandt have published the results of their labors.   Doisy and his co-workers were the first to isolate a crystalline estrogenic compound.   In his earlier work (80) (81) (82) (83), Marrian was really dealing with what we now call *theelol*, the trihydroxy compound, and the true relationship of theelol to theelin (the ketohydroxy compound) was finally shown by Butenandt.   Theelol, as well as theelin, is physiologically active, though there is still much debate as to the relative activity of the two (40).   The consensus of opinion seems to be that theelin is the more active.   Very recently Marrian (84) (85) has published a method which "includes the best features" of the methods of preparation by Doisy and by Butenandt, and also retains one or two of his own innovations.   From the same urine of pregnant women, theelol (the trihydroxyoestrin) is isolated as well as the theelin (the ketohydroxyoestrin).   First we shall present the method in schematic form (see page 170).

Now as to some details of the method.   It will be noticed that underlying the procedure is the fact, first, that the theelin is soluble in fat solvents, secondly, that it can be treated to a saponification process without destruction, and thirdly, that it can be recovered after saponification by first acidifying (in this case saturating the solution with CO_2) and extracting with ether.   Another interesting feature is that given an alcohol-benzene mixture, most of the theelol is taken up by the alcohol and almost all of the theelin by the benzene.

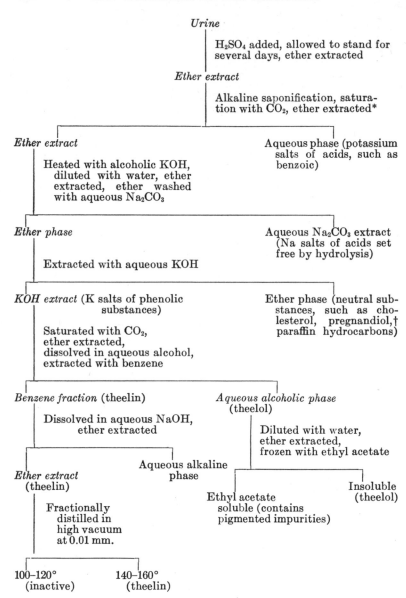

Urine

H₂SO₄ added, allowed to stand for several days, ether extracted

Ether extract

Alkaline saponification, saturation with CO₂, ether extracted*

Ether extract

Heated with alcoholic KOH, diluted with water, ether extracted, ether washed with aqueous Na₂CO₃

Aqueous phase (potassium salts of acids, such as benzoic)

Ether phase

Extracted with aqueous KOH

Aqueous Na₂CO₃ extract (Na salts of acids set free by hydrolysis)

KOH extract (K salts of phenolic substances)

Saturated with CO₂, ether extracted, dissolved in aqueous alcohol, extracted with benzene

Ether phase (neutral substances, such as cholesterol, pregnandiol,† paraffin hydrocarbons)

Benzene fraction (theelin)

Dissolved in aqueous NaOH, ether extracted

Aqueous alcoholic phase (theelol)

Diluted with water, ether extracted, frozen with ethyl acetate

Ether extract (theelin)

Fractionally distilled in high vacuum at 0.01 mm.

Aqueous alkaline phase

Ethyl acetate soluble (contains pigmented impurities)

Insoluble (theelol)

100–120° (inactive)

140–160° (theelin)

* If the requirements are an active extract rather than the pure hormone, one can stop at this stage and then merely evaporate off the ether and take up the residue in oil.

† See page **177**.

After acidifying and extracting with ether, the urine residue is discarded, and the ether extract is evaporated. This residue is saponified by heating for two hours with 5 per cent aqueous potassium hydroxide. The alkaline solution is saturated with CO_2 and thoroughly extracted with ether. The ether extract is next evaporated, heated with alcoholic hydrochloric acid, diluted with water and extracted with ether. The ether extract is now washed with aqueous sodium carbonate to remove more inactive material and then extracted with aqueous 5 per cent potassium hydroxide, which takes up the active (phenolic) fraction. To liberate the active material, the aqueous potassium hydroxide fraction is saturated with carbon dioxide and extracted with ether. The ether solution after washing with water is dissolved in 60 per cent aqueous ethyl alcohol and extracted with benzene. The benzene is washed with aqueous methyl alcohol.

To recover the theelol, the combined aqueous alcohol fractions are partially evaporated, diluted with water and extracted with ether. The ether is evaporated and the residue is chilled with a small amount of ethyl acetate, when crude theelol separates out. The impure crystals are decolorized by dissolving them in alcohol and boiling with charcoal. The material is filtered, the filtrate heated to remove the alcohol, and the residue is again treated with ice-cold ethyl acetate. Further purification is brought about by dissolving the crystals in alkali, filtering and precipitating with CO_2. The product is recrystallized from aqueous ethyl alcohol.

Going back to the theelin, which we have left dissolved in benzene, the solution is evaporated to dryness and the residue dissolved in a large volume of $N/100$ aqueous sodium hydroxide. It is possible, using this strength of alkali, to extract much of the theelin directly by repeated treatment with ether; in this way very much inactive material is left behind. The ether fraction, after washing, is evaporated and distilled *in vacuo*.

Doisy's method of preparation avoids the final use of distillation *in vacuo* (101) (49) (50).   In the first paper (101), Doisy points out that the essential steps in the process depend upon the solubility of the hormone in butyl alcohol, benzene, ethyl ether and dilute sodium hydroxide.   "We are aware that the extraction of an alkaline solution with ethyl ether does not give a quantitative recovery of hormone." However, this procedure ultimately led to the isolation of theelol from the alkaline extracts.   The outline is given below.

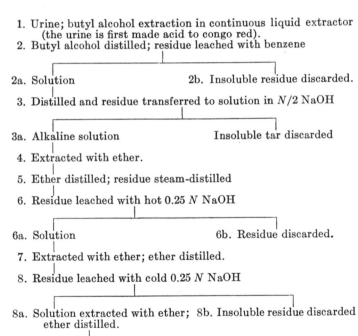

1. Urine; butyl alcohol extraction in continuous liquid extractor
   (the urine is first made acid to congo red).
2. Butyl alcohol distilled; residue leached with benzene

2a. Solution   2b. Insoluble residue discarded.

3. Distilled and residue transferred to solution in $N/2$ NaOH

3a. Alkaline solution   Insoluble tar discarded

4. Extracted with ether.

5. Ether distilled; residue steam-distilled

6. Residue leached with hot 0.25 N NaOH

6a. Solution   6b. Residue discarded.

7. Extracted with ether; ether distilled.

8. Residue leached with cold 0.25 N NaOH

8a. Solution extracted with ether; 8b. Insoluble residue discarded
    ether distilled.

9. Residue crystallized from hot 25 per cent ethyl alcohol or butyl
   alcohol.

In the next paper (49) Doisy records the isolation of theelol.   "Though a loss occurs in Step 4 (see above outline), we have focussed our attention thus far on Step 7. It was found that after extraction with ether the alkaline solution of Step 7 contained a large proportion of estrogenic substance. Upon acidification a precipitate which was partially soluble in ether usually formed. A test of this solution with spayed rats showed it to be active. Various procedures were instituted to obtain pure crystalline theelin but without success. The estrogenic substance of this fraction seemed to differ from theelin." This fraction, in reality, contained theelol. The alkaline solution of Step 7 is faintly acidified and gently heated to remove the ether, cooled, the brown precipitate is dissolved in alcohol, the solution is concentrated, and a brown semi-crystalline mass separates out on cooling. The crystals are decolorized with norit and recrystallized from alcohol.[4]

BUTENANDT

Quite independently, Butenandt had been working upon the isolation of the female hormone. He not only succeeded in doing this but he showed that the crystalline products obtained by Marrian in his earlier work were not theelin but theelol crystals. But Butenandt's most brilliant achievement was to show that theelol could be distilled with potassium acid sulfate and quantitatively converted to theelin (20) (14). The chart on page 174 shows his work in schematic outline.

DINGEMANSE (43) (44)

The urine of pregnant women, several days old, and therefore alkaline, is extracted with benzene,[5] the benzene extract is reduced to a small volume, and fuller's earth to the extent

---

[4] In a very recent paper (79) an improved method for the purification of theelol is described. The purification of theelol via its sodium salt is very satisfactory.

[5] It seems to be the general consensus of opinion that much better yields are obtained by extracting an acidified urine.

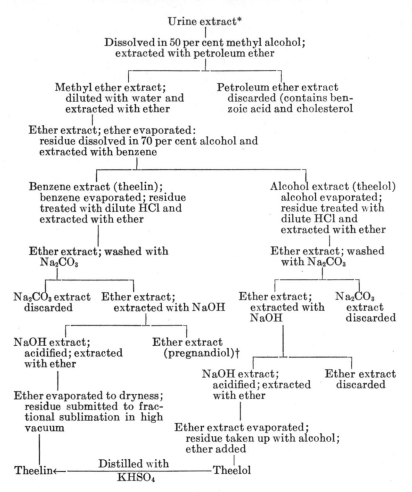

Urine extract*

Dissolved in 50 per cent methyl alcohol;
extracted with petroleum ether

Methyl ether extract;
diluted with water and
extracted with ether

Petroleum ether extract
discarded (contains ben-
zoic acid and cholesterol

Ether extract; ether evaporated:
residue dissolved in 70 per cent alcohol and
extracted with benzene

Benzene extract (theelin);
benzene evaporated; residue
treated with dilute HCl and
extracted with ether

Alcohol extract (theelol)
alcohol evaporated;
residue treated with
dilute HCl and
extracted with ether

Ether extract; washed with
Na₂CO₃

Ether extract; washed
with Na₂CO₃

Na₂CO₃ extract
discarded

Ether extract;
extracted with NaOH

Ether extract;
extracted with
NaOH

Na₂CO₃
extract
discarded

NaOH extract;
acidified; extracted
with ether

Ether extract
(pregnandiol)†

NaOH extract;
acidified; extracted
with ether

Ether extract
discarded

Ether evaporated to dryness;
residue submitted to fractional sublimation in high
vacuum

Ether extract evaporated;
residue taken up with alcohol;
ether added

Theelin ← ——— Distilled with ——— Theelol
                        KHSO₄

---

* The raw material was obtained from Schering-Kahlbaum. While no particulars are given, this undoubtedly represents a crude active fraction.
  † See page 177.

of twice the weight of the dry residue, is added. The clay mixture is boiled three times with benzene under reflux, and the combined benzene extracts are evaporated to a small volume. The solution is poured into boiling petroleum ether (40° to 60°C.) and kept at 0°C. for one night. The supernatant fluid is now poured off, and the precipitate is redissolved in benzene and 70 per cent alkaline alcohol is added. (The weight of the potassium hydroxide added to the alcohol is equal to the dry residue of the substance dissolved in benzene.) After thorough shaking, the benzene is removed; this benzene extract contains the bulk of the impurities and little hormone. The alcoholic solution is now acidified and again extracted with benzene. All of the hormone goes into the benzene solution.

The benzene extract is washed with 10 per cent sodium carbonate. The treatment with 70 per cent alcohol, described above, is repeated twice. After the final extraction with benzene, the 70 per cent alkaline alcoholic extract is evaporated until all the alcohol disappears. The remaining watery alkaline solution is filtered through asbestos and extracted with benzene. After acidifying the benzene solution, it is washed with water. On concentrating the benzene solution, white or brownish yellow crystals appear. The crystals may be purified by boiling a benzene solution with norit.[6]

THEELIN FROM MARE'S URINE

Curtis (39), making use of Zondek's observation (105), that the urine of pregnant mares contains relatively large quantities of theelin, has developed the following method of preparation: The urine is acidified to pH 1 with hydrochloric acid and kept at room temperature for a week. Five to 15 grams of sodium benzoate per liter of urine are added; the urine is filtered and the precipitate dried. The precipitate is extracted with ether. The ether solution is washed with strong sodium hydroxide until the pH of the aqueous

[6] Incidentally, in this paper, Dingemanse points out an approximate method for separating the male and female hormones. In a mixture of benzene and alcoholic potassium hydroxide, the male hormone goes into the former, whereas 90 per cent of the female hormone remains with the alkali.

phase is 8.5 to 9. The aqueous washings are extracted with ether. The ether extracts are combined and distilled. The residue is taken up in equal parts of butyl alcohol and petroleum ether, and this solution is washed with sodium carbonate. The estrus-producing material is extracted from the organic solvents with dilute alkali. The alkaline solution is acidified and extracted with ether. The ether extract is distilled. The residue is dissolved in alcohol and treated with semicarbazide. The semicarbazone is recrystallized from aqueous alcohol. Ten gallons of urine yield 1 gram of theelin.

THE RELATION OF THEELIN TO THEELOL

We owe to Butenandt the important discovery that theelol can be converted to theelin by distilling the former in high vacuum with potassium acid sulfate, with the loss of the elements of water (20). This was further confirmed by Marrian (86) (84), who showed that the monomethyl-ether of theelol can be dehydrated to yield a product identical with the monomethyl ether of theelin.

CHEMICAL AND PHYSICAL PROPERTIES OF THEELIN

Theelin has the formula $C_{18}H_{22}O_2$, with a melting point of 253° to 254° (uncorrected). The preparation of a monooxime and monoacetate point to a keto and a hydroxyl group (15). Theelin is soluble in chloroform, benzene, alcohol, acetone and ether. It is somewhat less soluble in petroleum ether and very little soluble in water. It is insoluble in bicarbonate and carbonate solutions but soluble in sodium hydroxide. Besides the oxime and the acetate, the monomethyl ether (97) (48) and the semicarbazone (17) have been prepared. On catalytic hydrogenation, theelin is converted into a reduction product, $C_{18}H_{30}O$, indicating the presence of three double bonds in the molecule (15); though, on the other hand, the iodine value of the monomethyl ether of theelin points to one double bond (84). The specific rotation is (in alcohol) $(\alpha)_D$ + 157° (in chloroform) $(\alpha)_D$ + 156° and the absorption spectrum is well defined in the ultra-violet at 283–285mμ (48) (84). It gives a positive Millon's reaction. The acidity of theelin is due to the −OH group, since its esters are insoluble in alkali, while derivatives involving the carbonyl group remain soluble (86) (23).

CHEMICAL AND PHYSICAL PROPERTIES OF THEELOL

The formula is $C_{18}H_{24}O_3$, with a melting point of 273° to 274°. It is fairly soluble in alcohol and acetone, less soluble in ether and ethyl acetate, and still less soluble in petroleum ether. It dissolves readily in dilute alkalis. Its specific rotation is (in pyridine) (α) 5461 + 38.5° and (in alcohol) $[(\alpha)]_D^{27}$ + 61. It forms a triacetate, indicating three OH groups, and also a monomethyl ether. The iodine value indicates the presence of one double bond (84) (48) (83) (86) (96a). It is converted into theelin when distilled with potassium acid sulfate, losing a molecule of water in the process.

PREGNANDIOL

Marrian in 1929 isolated an inactive alcohol in the unsaponifiable fraction of the ether-soluble material (80) to which Butenandt later (13) (16) gave the name *pregnandiol*. This compound is of particular interest to us because it has been the means of a working hypothesis with regard to the structural formulas of theelin and theelol.

Pregnandiol has the formula $C_{21}H_{36}O_2$. It can be oxidised to a diketone, $C_{21}H_{32}O_2$, indicating that both OH groups are secondary. The ketone gives a positive iodoform reaction, indicating a −CO−CH$_3$ group, and also the presence of −CH-(OH)−CH$_3$ group in pregnandiol. The diketone can be reduced to the saturated hydrocarbon, pregnane, $C_{21}H_{36}$. Butenandt has shown the relation of this pregnane to the bile acids and the sterols by starting with the ethyl ester of cholanic acid and ultimately getting pregnane; and the following formula for pregnandiol is suggested (84) (18):

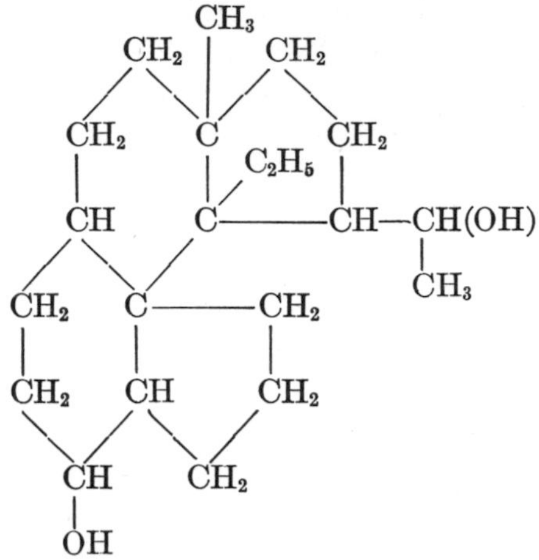

On the basis of this work, and on the supposition of a close chemical relationship between the sterols, the bile acids, pregnandiol and theelin, the formula for the latter and for theelol was postulated (13) (16):[7]

[7] Very recently, Rosenheim and King have advanced the theory that the basic ring structure of the sterols and bile acids is

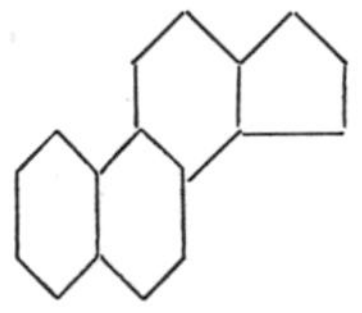

Are theelin and theelol derived from sterols and the bile acids of the body?

It is suggested that the naming of the estrin group be based on the parent saturated hydrocarbon, estrane, $C_{18}H_{30}$; or

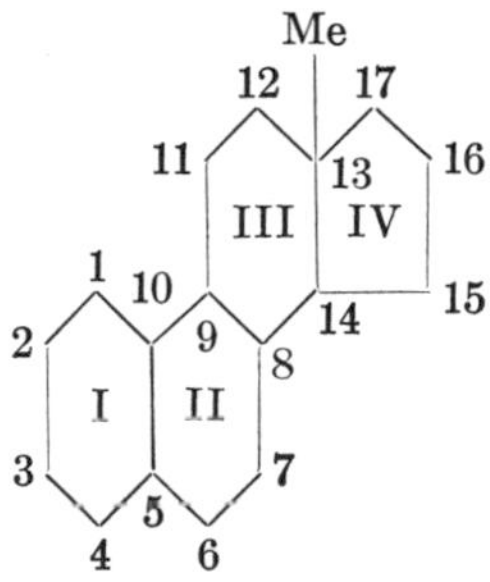

Trihydroxyestrin might be called *estriol* and ketohydroxyestrin, *estrone*.

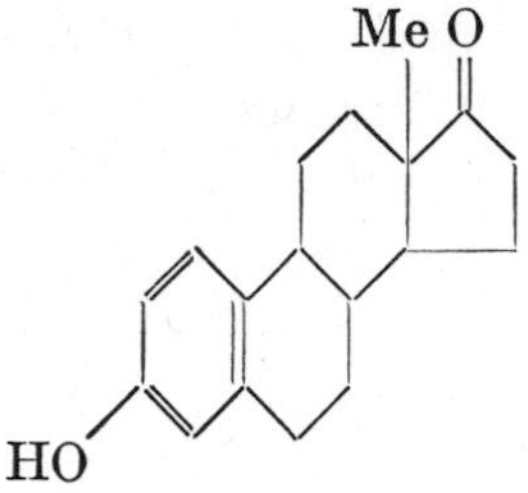

Me O

HO

Theelin

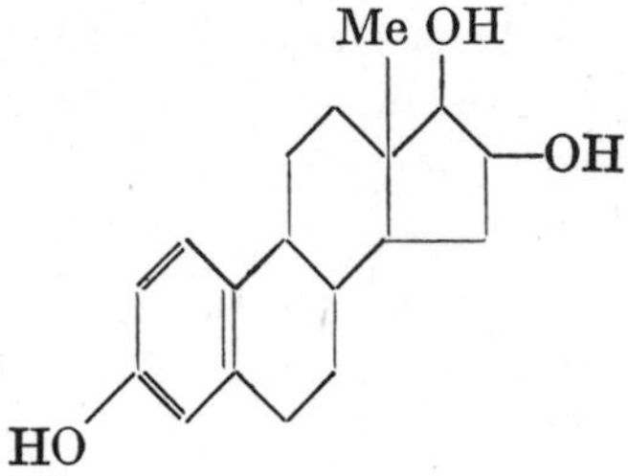

Me OH

—OH

HO

Theelol

Recently (85) Butenandt has obtained further evidence of the correctness of his structural formulas by first converting theelol into a phenol dicarboxylic acid, $C_{18}H_{22}O_5$ by alkaline fusion, and then, by dehydrogenation with selenium and elimination of carbon dioxide, converting the acid into dimethylphenanthrol, $C_{16}H_{13}OH$. This dimethyl derivative was converted into dimethylphenanthrene by means of zinc dust:

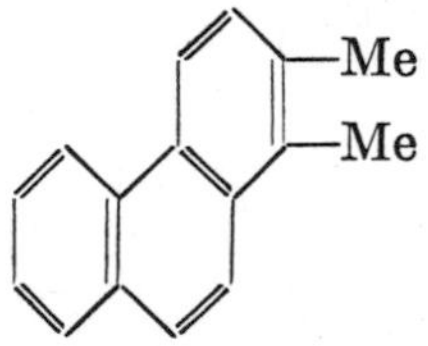

—Me
—Me

The dimethylphenanthrene was also prepared synthetically, and from etiobilianic acid (a bile acid derivative).

Examination of unimolecular films of theelin derivatives and crystallographic examination lend support to the structures for theelin and theelol proposed by Butenandt (85) (87) (1) (41); and rather striking evidence is brought forward by Cook and Dodds (85) (35) (34) (35a) to show that several synthetic compounds, possibly related to theelin, possess estrus-exciting properties. For example, 1-keto-1:2:3:4-tetrahydrophenanthrene,

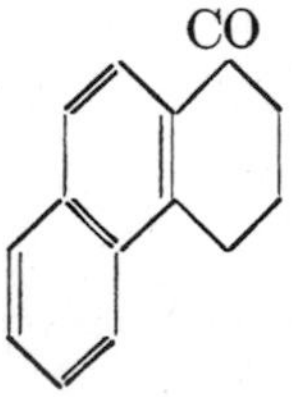

CO

which contains its keto group in relatively the same position as theelin, is active. "Correlation of oestrogenic activity with cancer-producing activity was achieved in the case 9:10-dihydroxy-9:10-di-*n*-butyl-9:10-dihydro-1:2:5:6-dibenzanthracene," a compound derived from 1:2:5:6-dibenzanthracene, which though carcinogenic is not estrogenic. Positive results were also obtained among the sterols: neo-ergosterol, ergosterol, and calciferol.[8]

[8] An excellent discussion of the various steps involved in the chemistry of theelin is given by Marrian (87).

Hydrocarbons containing the ring system present in the sterols, bile acids and the ovarian (and male?) hormone have recently been synthetically produced in a very striking way. Cook and Hewett (35a) condense the Grignard compound of β-l-naphthylethyl chloride with cyclopentanone to yield a carbinol (I) which is dehydrated with KHSO₄ to give l-(β-l'-naphthylethyl)-Δ'-*cyclopentene* (II); and this is isomerised by aluminum chloride or stannic chloride into 1:2-cyclo*pentano*-1:2:3:4-tetrahydrophenanthrene (III), a ring system present in sterols, bile acids and the ovarian and male (?) hormones:

I   II   III

When (I) is treated with sulfuric acid at 100°, dehydrogenation takes place, sulfur dioxide is liberated and 1:2-*cyclo*pentenophenanthrene (IV) is formed

IV

ISOMERIC ESTRUS-PRODUCING SUBSTANCES

Butenandt (22) finds that when theelol is distilled with potassium acid sulfate two isomeric substances are obtained from human (pregnant) urine, and the β-form, one-sixth as active, is identical with a substance obtained from the urine of pregnant mares (which, incidentally, seems to be a very rich source for female hormones). Schwenk (94b) and Girard (61a) (61b) (61c), (94a), claim to have isolated three other active substances from mare's urine. The substances and their properties may be summarized (22) (11) (98):

SUBSTANCE	ROTATION	MELTING POINT	BENZOATE MELTING POINT	OXIME MELTING POINT
α-form............	$[(\alpha)]_D^{18}$ 157°(CHCl$_3$)	251°	217.5°	230°?
β-form.............	$[(\alpha)]_D^{18}$ 165°(CHCl$_3$	257°	205°	
δ-form.............	$[(\alpha)]_D^{18}$ 46°(CHCl$_3$)	209°	177°	None
Equiline............	$[(\alpha)]_D^{15}$ 308°(dioxane)	239°	197°	222°
Hippuline..........	$[(\alpha)]_D^{15}$ 128°(dioxane)	233°		
Equilenine.........	$[(\alpha)]_D^{16}$ 87°(dioxane)	258°	222°	249°

AN INTERNATIONAL UNIT

The Health Organization of the League of Nations has selected the ketohydroxy form of the hormone in pure crystalline condition for standardization. The unit of activity is defined as that contained in 0.0001 mg. of the substance (*J. Am. Med. Assoc.*, **101**, 377 (1933)).

COLORIMETRIC ESTIMATION

An attempt to develop a colorimetric method for estimating theelin has been proposed by Kober (72) (84). To 5γ of crystalline theelin, 0.2 cc. of a mixture of equal parts of concentrated H$_2$SO$_4$ and phenolsulfonic acid is added. This is warmed in a boiling water-bath, cooled, 0.2 cc. of water is added, the mixture heated again (to boiling), diluted with 0.6 cc. of water and cooled. The final mixture is a clear red solution which can be measured with a standard solution of cresol red. Five γ of the hormone gives about the same color as 25 γ of cresol red.

EQUOL

Marrian has isolated from the urine of the pregnant mares an inactive phenol, $C_{15}H_{12}O(OH)_2$, M.P. 189–190.5°, $[(\alpha)_{5461}]$ = −21.5° (88). In what way this substance is related to theelin, if at all, is entirely unknown at present. Marrian has also isolated a new triol from the urine of pregnant mares, $C_2H_{46}O_6$ (94c).

BIOLOGICAL PROPERTIES AND CLINICAL APPLICATIONS OF
THEELIN

These are discussed in the following references: (106) (91) (62) (59) (60) (92) (46) (93) (3) (73) (47) (90) (4) (64).

AQUEOUS EXTRACTS OF THEELIN

Despite the fact that theelin is but slightly soluble in water, active watery extracts have been prepared. Since many of these aqueous extracts were prepared some years ago, when little was known about the chemistry of theelin itself, there is still much confusion as to the exact physiological potencies of such material (45) (46) (2) (74) (75).

ESTROGENIC SUBSTANCES IN PLANTS

Several workers (78) (51) (59) have claimed that extracts of various plant products contain active material. Walker and Janney (102) record positive results with extracts of alder leaves and catkins, willow catkins, sprouted oats and rhubarb leaves. The extract was prepared by allowing the fresh material to stand covered with 95 per cent alcohol for several days at room temperature. The liquid was pressed from the solid portions and evaporated to small volume. The solid material was strained through cheese cloth, the filtrate was evaporated until the alcohol was removed and the remaining sludge was made alkaline with sodium carbonate and extracted with ether. The ether extract was evaporated and the residue taken up in physiological salt solution and injected into castrated mice (71). Negative results were obtained with the following: apples, beets, cabbage, carrots, corn, grapes, peaches, plums, potatoes, spinach, sweet potatoes, Swiss chard and tomatoes. Further, carotin, chlorophyll, inositol, phytin, saponin and urson yielded negative results.

In a recent publication (21), Butenandt describes the isolation of a crystalline product from the expressed residue of palm leaves which is in every way identical with theelin (or, more specifically, with one of its isomers, the α-form (see p. 216).

PROGESTIN (OR CORPORIN): THE CORPUS LUTEUM HORMONE

We have already stated that theelin (and theelol) cannot be regarded as the sole female hormone. We have indicated that one of the hormones of the anterior pituitary also plays its part in the sex cycle (p. 71). But recent work by Corner, Hisaw and their associates make it quite certain that the corpus luteum develops an internal secretion (the *corporin* of Hisaw and the *progestin* of Corner) which acts only after ovulation, at about the middle of the intermenstrual period. "This secretion causes the endometrium to progress from the proliferative stage to the secretory or progravid stage, which reaches its greatest development just before menstruation occurs" (8). Theelin cannot bring about all the changes in the endometrium necessary for a complete monthly cycle. Both theelin and progestin have no effect on the ovaries; their action is purely substitutional. Progestin cannot act on the endometrium unless the latter has been prepared by theelin. The menstrual bleeding is the result of the action of both theelin and progestin; and these, in turn, are under the control of the anterior pituitary.

Hisaw in 1927 prepared an acid-alcoholic extract of sow corpora lutea which produced modifications characteristic of pregnancy in the rat endometrium (65). Using lipoid extracts, Corner (37) showed that these produced changes typical of early pregnancy and pseudopregnancy in the uterus of castrate rabbits. Rabbits castrated during estrus were given subcutaneous injections of the lipoid extract. Within five days there resulted progestational changes in the endometrium similar to that present in the uterus during pseudopregnancy or early pregnancy. The effect was undoubtedly due to a specific corpus luteum hormone. Hisaw's preparation produced relaxation in the pelvis of the guinea pig, but Corner's extract failed to do so. Further work showed that Hisaw's extract, in reality, contained two hormones: *relaxin*, to which the pelvic relaxation must be attributed; and *corporin*, apparently identical with Corner's progestin (69). Progestion or corporin, has also been called the *beta-factor* and *lutin* (67).

In a recent publication (55), Hisaw claims that the corpus luteum contains three active hormones: *relaxin*, which has a specific action on the pelvic ligaments; *progestin* (Hisaw's *corporin*), which produces a premenstrual endometrium in monkeys, the pseudopregnancy picture in the rabbit's uterus, and deciduomata; and a third (the mucifying hormone), which produces the mucification reaction. It is claimed, however, by Allen that this mucifying hormone is probably nothing else than theelin (7).

TEST METHODS

The relaxation reaction for *relaxin* is given in (66). Progestin is tested by the pseudopregnancy reaction in the rabbit (37) and the premenstrual picture in the monkey (70). The mucifying hormone is identified by the mucification of the vaginal mucosa (55). For relaxin, the guinea pig unit is the minimum amount of hormone which causes a definite loosening of the ligaments within ten to twelve hours after a single injection (58). A rabbit unit of progestin is that amount of the active substance which brings about a very good pseudo-pregnancy picture in the rabbit's uterus when injected over a period of four days following castration in heat (55). Corner (37) (7) tests his extract by injecting it into the adult, recently castrated female rabbit for five days, with autopsy on the sixth day and study of histological sections of the uterus. A rat unit of the mucifying hormone is that amount of extract which brings about a mucified condition of the rat's vagina similar to that of a six or seven day pseudopregnancy when injected over a period of four days following castration in full oestrum and killed on the fifth day (55). For a further possible test, see (63).

METHOD OF PREPARING AN ACTIVE EXTRACT OF PROGESTIN
(55) (7) (58) (68) (56) (57) (54)

The corpora lutea is dissected from fresh sow's ovaries, the lutein tissue (1 kg.) is extracted twice at room temperature with 2-liter portions of acidulated alcohol (20 cc. concentrated hydrochloric acid per liter). The extracts are removed by pressing and the residual tissue is refluxed with $1\frac{1}{2}$ liters of acidulated alcohol for one hour. The extracts are combined, neutralized to pH 6.8 to 7, filtered, and the precipitate redissolved (in acid alcohol), reprecipitated (at pH 6.8 to 7) and the final precipitate discarded. The extracts are evaporated to a thick paste under reduced pressure (55). The residue is extracted with 500 cc. of 95 per cent alcohol. The alcoholic extract is evaporated to dryness, emulsified in water, and phospholipins eliminated by the addition of acetone. The lipins are filtered off, the solution is evaporated and again taken up in 95 per cent alcohol. If a crude active extract of progestin is needed, the residue instead of being taken up with alcohol may be treated with oil and the oil emulsion used for injection. If, however, the three hormones are to be separated from one another, the 95 per cent alcoholic extract (which contains all three hormones) is evaporated to dryness and extracted with 99 per cent alcohol. The solution is allowed to stand for several hours, and the precipitate (which contains practically all the relaxin) is centrifuged off. For a further purification of relaxin, see (58).

The alcoholic solution is evaporated to a small volume and 100 cc. of ether is added. The precipitate which settles contains a large part of the mucifying hormone. The ether extract is evaporated to dryness and the residue again extracted with 100 cc. ether. A second (smaller) precipitate of the mucifying hormone settles out. This process is repeated until no more precipitate appears.

We have, then, an alcohol-insoluble fraction, (relaxin) an alcohol-soluble but ether-insoluble fraction (mucifying hormone) and an alcohol-soluble and ether-soluble fraction (progestin). For further purification, see (54) (55).

Corner and Allen extract the progestin with boiling alcohol (7). The alcoholic extract is distilled to a thick sludge and extracted with ether. The ether soluble portion is evaporated to 200 and 800 cc. acetone are added. The precipitate is redissolved in ether and reprecipitated with acetone. The acetone-soluble portion is distilled to a thick oil *in vacuo* and the residue is dissolved in alcohol. This yields a potent extract. The material may be purified still further (36).

Any theelin in a progestin solution may be separated by extracting the solution (in 33 per cent alcohol) three times with 0.5 times its volume of petroleum ether. Practically all of the progestin is found in the petroleum ether layer (7a).

PROPERTIES

Progestin is slightly soluble in water and more soluble in aqueous alkaline solutions. It is soluble in organic solvents such as acetone, ethyl alcohol, methyl alcohol, pyridine,

benzene, ether, petroleum ether and chloroform.   It is stable
in non-oxidizing acids and very unstable in alkalis.   Oxidation destroys progestin and it deteriorates in the presence
of atmospheric oxygen at room temperature.

Relaxin is soluble in acid and aqueous alkaline solutions
and in water.   It is insoluble in fat solvents such as acetone,
ether, petroleum ether, 100 per cent alcohol and benzine.
In non-oxidizing acids, relaxin is stable, but in alkalis it is
unstable.   It is destroyed above 80°C.

So far progestin has only been prepared from corpora lutea.
It is quite inaffective by mouth (7).

Turner and Frank are of the opinion that the growth of the
mammary glands during pregnancy comes as a result of the
combined action of theelin and one or more hormones from
the corpus luteum (100) (99).

For the rôle of progestin in the female reproductive cycle,
and for possible clinical applications, see (95) (91) (67) (36).

PLACENTAL HORMONES

Collip, basing his work on that of Wiesner (103), succeeded
in 1930 in preparing a placental extract which differed from
theelin in its properties (29) (31) (36) (28) (70).   Unlike
theelin, it was insoluble in ether, and, unlike theelin, it failed to
produce estrus in the ovariectomised animal.[9]   By means
of an acetone extraction, Collip obtained two active fractions,
apart from the ether-soluble theelin (32).   The alcohol-
soluble fraction, to which the name *emmenin* was given, was
found to be active orally and to cause premature estrus in
immature female rats.   The alcohol-insoluble fraction, an
anterior pituitary-like substance, caused premature estrus
in immature female rats (31a).   Browne, working in Collip's
laboratroy, and using Marrian's method for isolating theelol,
obtained emmenin in crystalline form (11).   Quite recently,
in conjunction with Butenandt, Browne made a careful

[9] In later work, by using large doses, estrus was obtained.

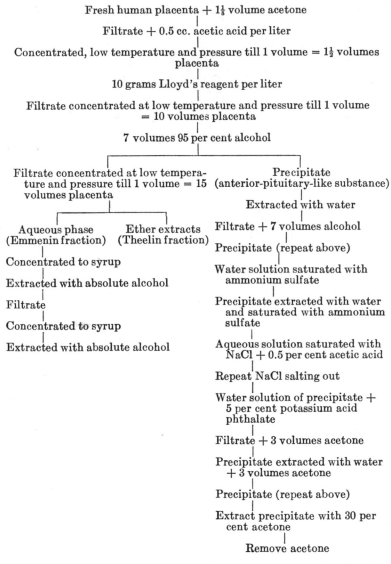

Fresh human placenta + 1⅓ volume acetone

Filtrate + 0.5 cc. acetic acid per liter

Concentrated, low temperature and pressure till 1 volume = 1½ volumes placenta

10 grams Lloyd's reagent per liter

Filtrate concentrated at low temperature and pressure till 1 volume = 10 volumes placenta

7 volumes 95 per cent alcohol

Filtrate concentrated at low temperature and pressure till 1 volume = 15 volumes placenta

Precipitate (anterior-pituitary-like substance)

Extracted with water

Aqueous phase (Emmenin fraction)   Ether extracts (Theelin fraction)

Filtrate + 7 volumes alcohol

Concentrated to syrup

Precipitate (repeat above)

Extracted with absolute alcohol

Water solution saturated with ammonium sulfate

Filtrate

Precipitate extracted with water and saturated with ammonium sulfate

Concentrated to syrup

Extracted with absolute alcohol

Aqueous solution saturated with NaCl + 0.5 per cent acetic acid

Repeat NaCl salting out

Water solution of precipitate + 5 per cent potassium acid phthalate

Filtrate + 3 volumes acetone

Precipitate extracted with water + 3 volumes acetone

Precipitate (repeat above)

Extract precipitate with 30 per cent acetone

Remove acetone

comparative study of Doisy's theelol, Butenandt's theelol. ("Follikelhormonhydrat") and emmenin (19), all three having the formula $C_{18}H_{24}O_3$; with the result that Butenandt and

Browne are of the opinion that the three substances are identical.

Collip's method of obtaining active fractions may be given in outline form (32) (30) (33) (see chart on page 188).

For biological and clinical studies, see (29) (33) (26) (25).

REFERENCES

(1) ADAM, N. K., DANIELLI, J. F., HASLEWOOD, G. A. D., AND MARRIAN, G. F.: Surface films of oestrin derivatives. *Biochem. J.*, **26**, 1233 (1932).

(2) ALLAN, D., DICKENS, F., DODDS, E. C., AND HOWITT, F. O.: A study of the oestrus-producing hormone: its preparation and standardisation in a water-soluble form. *Biochem. J.*, **22**, 1526 (1928).

(3) ALLEN, E.: Endocrine activity of the ovary. *J. Am. Med. Assoc.*, **97**, 1189 (1931).

(4) ALLEN, E.: Ovarian follicular hormone, theelin; animal reactions. In Allen's *Sex and Internal Secretions*. (Williams & Wilkins, Baltimore. 1932.)

(5) ALLEN, E., AND DOISY, E. A.: An ovarian hormone. *J. Am. Med. Assoc.*, **81**, 819 (1923).

(6) ALLEN, E., AND DOISY, E. A.: Ovarian and placental hormones. *Physiol. Reviews*, **7**, 600 (1927).

(7) ALLEN, W. M.: The preparation of purified progestin. *J. Biol. Chem.*, **98**, 591 (1932).

(7a) ALLEN, W. M., AND MEYER, R. K.: The quantitative separation of progestin from estrin in extracts of the corpus luteum. *Am. J. Physiol.*, **106**, 55 (1933).

(8) ANON: Amenorrhea. *J. Am. Med. Assoc.*, **100**, 299 (1933).

(9) ANON: Estrogenic substances: theelin. *J. Am. Med. Assoc.*, **100**, 1131 (1933).

(10) ASCHHEIM, S., AND ZONDEK, B.: Hypophysenvorderlappenhormon und Ovarialhormon im Harn von Schwangeren. *Klin. Woch.*, **6**, 1322 (1927).

(10a) BOGERT, M. T., AND DAVIDSON, D.: The synthesis of condensed polynuclear hydrocarbons by the cyclodehydration of aromatic alcohols. I. Indanes. *J. Am. Chem. Soc.*, **56**, 185 (1934).

(11) BROWNE, J. S. L.: The chemical and physiological properties of crystalline oestrogenic hormones. *Canadian J. Research*, **8**, 180 (1933).

(12) BUGBEE, E. P., AND SIMOND, A. E.: Bio-assay of preparations of ovarian follicular hormone. *J. Am. Pharmac. Assoc.*, **17**, 962 (1928).

(13) BUTENANDT, A.: Ueber das Pregnandiol, einen neuen Sterin-Abkömmlung aus Schwangeren-Harn. *Ber. deutsch. chem. Gesel.*, **63**, 659 (1930).

(14) BUTENANDT, A.: Ueber die Reindarstellung des Follikelhormons aus Schwangerenharn. *Zt. physiol. Chem.*, **191**, 127 (1930).

(15) BUTENANDT, A.: Ueber physikalische und chemische Eigenschaften des krystallisierten Follikehormons. *Zt. physiol. Chem.*, **191**, 140 (1930).

(16) BUTENANDT, A.: Ueber das Pregnandiol. II. *Ber. deutsch. chem. Gesel.*, **64**, 2529 (1931).

(17) BUTENANDT, A.: Untersuchungen ueber das weibliche Sexualhormon. (Weidmannsche Buchhanglung, Berlin. 1931.)

(18) BUTENANDT, A.: Chemical constitution of the follicular and testicular hormones. *Nature*, Aug. 13 (1932).

(19) BUTENANDT, A., AND BROWNE, J. S. L.: Vergleichende Untersuchung von Theelol, Emmenin und Follikelhormonhydrat. *Zt. physiol. Chem.*, **216**, 49 (1933).

(20) BUTENANDT, A., AND HILDEBRANDT, F.: Ueber ein zweites Hormonkrystallisat aus Schwangerenharn und seine physiologischen und chemischen Beziehungen zum krystallisierten Follikelhormon. *Zt. physiol. Chem.*, **199**, 243 (1931).

(21) BUTENANDT, A., AND JACOBI, H.: Ueber die Darstellung eines krystallisierten pflanzlichen Tokohinins (Thelykinins) und seine Identifizierung mit dem α-Follikelhormon. *Zt. physiol. Chem.*, **218**, 104 (1933).

(22) BUTENANDT, A., AND STOERMER, I.: Ueber isomere Follikelhormone. *Zt. physiol. Chem.*, **208**, 129 (1932).

(23) BUTENANDT, A., STOERMER, I., AND WESTPHAL, U.: Beiträege zur Konstitutionsermittlung des Follikelhormons. I. *Zt. physiol. Chem.*, **208**, 149 (1932).

(24) BUTENANDT, A., AND ZIEGNER, E. VON: Ueber die physiologische Wirksamkeit des Krystallisierten weiblichen Sexualhormons im Allen-Doisy-Test. *Zt. physiol. Chem.*, **188**, 1 (1930).

(25) CAMPBELL, A. D., AND COLLIP, J. B.: Notes on the clinical use of certain placental extracts. *Canadian Med. Assoc. J.*, **23**, 633 (1930).

(26) CAMPBELL, A. D., AND COLLIP, J. B.: Further clinical studies on the anterior-pituitary-like hormone of the human placenta. *Canadian Med. Assoc. J.*, **25**, 9 (1931).

(27) COLLIP J. C.: The ovary stimulating hormone of the placenta. *Nature* (1930), March 22.

(28) COLLIP, J. B.: Placental hormones. *Proc. California Acad. Med.* (1930).

(29) COLLIP, J. B.: Sex hormones of the female. *Canadian Med. Assoc. J.*, **22**, 212 (1930).

(30) COLLIP, J. B.: Further observations on an ovary-stimulatng hormone of the placenta. *Canadian Med. Assoc. J.*, **22**, 761 (1930).

(31) COLLIP, J. B.: Placental hormones. *Canadian Med. Assoc. J.*, **23**, 631 (1930).

(31a) COLLIP, J. B., SELYE, H., ANDERSON, E. M., AND THOMPSON, D. L.:
Production of èstrus. Relationship between active principles of
the placenta and pregnancy blood and urine and those of the
anterior pituitary. *J. Am. Med. Assoc.*, **101**, 1553 (1933).

(32) COLLIP, J. B., THOMPSON, D. L., BROWNE, J. S. L., McPHAIL, M. K.,
AND WILLIAMSON, J. E.: Placental hormones. *Endocrinology*, **15**,
315 (1931).

(33) COLLIP, J. B., THOMSON, D. L., McPHAIL, M. K., AND WILLIAMSON,
J. E.: The anterior-pituitary-like hormone of the human placenta.
Canadian Med. Assoc. J., **24**, 201 (1931).

(34) COOK, J. W., AND DODDS, E. C.: Sex hormones and cancer-producing
compounds. *Nature*, **131**, 205 (1933).

(35) COOK, J. W., DODDS, E. C., AND HEWETT, C. L.: A synthetic oestrus-
exciting compound. *Nature*, **131**, 56 (1933).

(35a) COOK, J. W., AND HEWETT, C. L.: The synthesis of compounds related to the sterols, bile acids and oestrus-producing hormones.
Part I. 1:2-cyclopentanophenanthrene. *J. Chem. Soc.*, August
(1933), p. 1098.

(36) CORNER, G. W.: The nature of the menstrual cycle. *Medicine*, **12**,
61 (1933).

(37) CORNER, G. W., AND ALLEN, W. M.: Physiology of the corpus luteum.
II. Production of a special uterine reaction (progrestational proliferation) by extracts of the corpus luteum. *Am. J. Physiol.*,
88, 326 (1929).

(38) COWARD, K. H., AND BURN, J. H.: The variation in the unit of the
oestrus-producing hormone. *J. Physiol.*, **63**, 270 (1927).

(39) CURTIS, J. M.: A rapid method for the preparation of theelin. *Proc.
Amer. Soc. Biol. Chemists*, **8**, 33 (1933).

(40) CURTIS, J. M., AND DOISY, E. A.: The bioassay of theelol. *J. Biol.
Chem.*, **91**, 647 (1931).

(41) DANIELLI, J. F., MARRIAN, G. F., AND HASLEWOOD, G. A. D.: Further observations on surface films of oestrin derivatives and of
pregnandiol. *Biochem. J.*, **27**, 311 (1933).

(42) DICKENS, F., DODDS, E. C., AND WRIGHT, S.: Observations upon the
preparation and standardisation of the ovarian hormone. *Biochem. J.*, **19**, 853 (1925).

(43) DINGEMANSE, E.: On crystalline menformon, the method of its production, its biological properties and its isolation from the male
hormone. *Proc. Second International Congress for Sex Research*,
1930.

(44) DINGEMANSE, E., JONGH DE, S. E., AND LAQUEUR, E.: Ueber krystal-
linisches Menformon. *Deut. Med. Wochensehr.*, Nr. 8 (1930).

(45) DODDS, E. C.: The ovarian hormone. *Lancet*, June 2, p. 1107 (1928).

(46) DODDS, E. C.: The clinical importance of the sex hormones. *Am. J.
Obstet. and Gynecol.*, **22**, 520 (1931).

(47) Dodds, E. C., and Dickens, F.: The hormones of the female reproductive cycle. *J. Obstet. and Gyn.*, **36** (1929).

(48) Doisy, E. A.: Biochemistry of the follicular hormone, theelin. In
Allen's *Sex and Internal Secretions.* (Williams & Wilkins, Baltimore. 1932.)

(49) Doisy, E. A., and Thayer, S. A.: The preparation of theelol. *J.
Biol. Chem.*, **91**, 641 (1931).

(50) Doisy, E. A., Veler, C. D., and Thayer, S.: The preparation of the
crystalline ovarian hormone from the urine of pregnant women.
J. Biol. Chem., **86**, 499 (1930).

(51) Dorn, M., Faure, W., Poll, H., and Blotevogel, W.: Tokokinine
stoffe mit sexualhormonartiger Wirkung aus Pflanzenzellen. *Med.
Klin.*, **22**, 1886 (1926).

(52) Fee, A. R., Marrian, G. F., and Parkes, A. S.: The significance of
the occurrence of oestrin in male urine. *J. Physiol.*, **67**, 377 (1929).

(53) Fevold, H. L.: The chemical nature of the ovarian and the gonadotropic hormones. *J. Chem. Educ.*, **10**, 174 (1933).

(54) Fevold, H. L., and Hisaw, F. L.: Purification of corporin. *Proc.
Soc. Exp. Biol. and Med.*, **29**, 620 (1932).

(55) Fevold, H. L., Hisaw, F. L., and Leonard, S. L.: Hormones of the
corpus luteum. The separation and purification of three active
substances. *J. Am. Chem. Soc.*, **54**, 254 (1932).

(56) Fevold, H. L., Hisaw, F. L., and Meyer, R. K.: Isolation of the
relaxative hormone of the corpus luteum. *Proc. Soc. Exp. Biol.
& Med.*, **27**, 604 (1930).

(57) Fevold, H. L., Hisaw, F. L., and Meyer, R. K.: Purification of
hormone of corpus luteum responsible for progestational development and other reactions. *Proc. Soc. Exp. Biol. & Med.*, **27**, 606
(1930).

(58) Fevold, H. L., Hisaw, F. L., and Meyer, R. K.: The relaxative
hormone of the corpus luteum. Its purification and concentration.
J. Am. Chem. Soc., **52**, 3340 (1930).

(59) Frank, R. T.: The female sex hormone. (C. C. Thomas, Spring-
field. 1929.)

(60) Frank, R. T.: The rôle of the female sex hormone. *J. Am. Med.
Assoc.*, **97**, 1852 (1931).

(61) Frank, R. T., and Goldberger, M. A.: The female sex hormone.
J. Am. Med. Assoc., **90**, 374 (1928).

(61a) Girard, A., Sandulesco, G., Friedenson, A., Gaudefroy, C., and
Rutgers, J. J.: Sur les hormones sexuelles cristallisées retirées
des l'urine des juments gravides. *Compt. Rend. de l'Acad. des
Scienc.*, **194**, 1020 (1932).

(61b) Girard, A., Sandulesco, G., Friedenson, A., and Rutgers, J. J.:
Sur une nouvelle hormone sexuelle cristallisée retirée de l'urine
des juments gravides. *Compt. Rend. del' Acad. des Scien.*, **194**,
909 (1932).

(61c) GIRARD, A., SANDULESCO, G., FRIEDENSON, A., AND RUTGERS, J. J.: Sur une nouvelle hormone sexuelle cristallisée. *Compt. Rend. de l'Acad. des Scienc.*, **195**, 981 (1932).

(62) GRAVES, W. P.: Female sex hormonology. (Saunders, Philadelphia. 1932.)

(63) HARRIS, R. G., AND NEWMAN, D. M.: A practical test for potency of extract of corpora lutea. *Science*, **74**, 182 (1931).

(64) HIRSCH, MAX: Handbuch der inneren Sekretion. (Curt Kabitsch, Leipzig. 1932.)

(65) HISAW, F. L.: Experimental relaxation of the symphysis pubis of the guinea pig. *Anat. Rec.*, **37**, 126 (1927).

(66) HISAW, F. L.: The corpus luteum hormone. I. Experimental relaxation of the pelvic ligaments of the guinea pig. *Physiol. Zool.*, **2**, 59 (1929).

(67) HISAW, F. L.: Physiology of the corpus luteum. Allen's *Sex and Internal Secretions* (Williams & Wilkins, Baltimore. 1932), p. 499.

(68) HISAW, F. L., FEVOLD, H. L., AND MEYER, R. K.: The corpus luteum hormone. II. Methods of extraction. *Physiol. Zool.*, **3**, 135 (1930).

(69) HISAW, F. L., FEVOLD, H. L., AND MEYER, R. K.: The function of the follicular and corpus luteum hormones in the production of a premenstrual endometrium in the uterus of castrate monkeys (Macacus rhesus). *Anat. Rec.*, **47**, 300 (1930).

(70) HISAW, F. L., MEYER, R. K., AND FEVOLD, H. L.: Production of a premenstrual endometrium in castrated monkeys by ovarian hormones. *Proc. Soc. Exp. Biol. & Med.*, **27**, 400 (1930).

(71) JANNEY, J. C., AND WALKER, B. S.: Estrogenic substances. I. Apparatus and methods for preparation of stable extracts from natural sources. *Endocrinology*, **14**, 101 (1930).

(72) KOBER, S.: Eine kolorimetrische Bestimmung des Brusthormons (Menformon). *Biochem. Zt.*, **239**, 209 (1931).

(73) KURZROK, R., AND RATNER, S.: The relation of amenorrhea accompanied by genital hypoplasia to the follicular hormone of the urine. *Am. J. Obst. & Gynecol.*, **23**, 689 (1932).

(74) LAQUEUR, E., HART, P. C., AND JONGH, DE, S. E.: Female sexual hormone (menformon). *Lancet*, May 28, p. 1126 (1927).

(75) LAQUEUR, E., AND JONGH, DE, S. E.: A female (sexual) hormone: menformon. *J. Am. Med. Assoc.*, **91**, 1169 (1928).

(76) LAQUEUR, E., AND JONGH, DE, S. E.: On the standardisation of the female sexual hormone, especially of pure water-soluble preparations (menformon). *J. Pharmacol. and Exp. Therap.*, **36**, 1 (1929).

(77) LEONARD, S. L., HISAW, F. L., AND FEVOLD, H. L.: Further studies on the follicular-corpus luteum hormone relationship in the rabbit. *Am. J. Physiol.*, **100**, 111 (1932).

(78) LOEWE, S., LANGE, F., AND SPOHR, E.: Ueber weibliche Sexualhormone (Thelytropine). XII. Brunsterzeugende Stoffe (Thelykinine) als Erzeugnisse des Pflanzenreiches. *Biochem. Zt.*, **180**, 1 (1927).

(79) MacCorquodale, D. W., Thayer, S. A., and Doisy, E. A.: On the purification and constitution of theelol. *J. Biol. Chem.*, **99**, 327 (1933).

(80) Marrian, G. F.: The chemistry of oestrin. I. Preparation from urine and separation from an unidentified solid alcohol. *Biochem. J.*, **23**, 1090 (1929).

(81) Marrian, G. F.: The chemistry of oestrin. II. Methods of purification. *Biochem. J.*, **23**, 1233 (1929).

(82) Marrian, G. F.: The chemistry of oestrin. III. An improved method of preparation and the isolation of active crystalline material. *Biochem. J.*, **24**, 435 (1930).

(83) Marrian, G. F.: The chemistry of oestrin. IV. The chemical nature of crystalline preparations. *Biochem. J.*, **24**, 1021 (1930).

(84) Marrian, G. F.: Recent advances in the chemistry and biological assay of oestrin. *Physiol. Reviews*, **13**, 185 (1933).

(85) Marrian, G. F., Danielli, J. F., Adam, N. K., Bernal, J. D., Butenandt, A., Dodds, E. C., and Cook, J. W.: The chemical constitution of oestrin. *J. Soc. Chem. Ind.*, **52** (1933), March 24.

(86) Marrian, G. F., and Haslewood, G. A.: The chemistry of oestrin. V. The mechanism of the conversion of trihydroxyoestrin into ketohydroxyoestrin. Marrian, G. F. and Haslewood, G. A. D.: *Biochem. J.*, 26, **25** (1932).

(87) Marrian, G. F., and Haslewood, G. A. D.: The chemistry of oestrin. VI. The ring structure of crystalline trihydroxy- and ketohydroxy-oestrin. *J. Soc. Chem. Ind.*, **51**, (1932), Aug. 19.

(88) Marrian, G. F., and Haslewood, G. A. D.: Equol, a new inactive phenol isolated from the ketohydroxyoestrin fraction of mares' urine. *Biochem. J.*, **26**, 1227 (1932).

(89) Marrian, G. F., and Parkes, A. S.: The assay of oestrin. *J. Physiol.*, **67**, 389 (1929).

(90) Marrian, G. F., and Parkes, A. S.: The relative amounts of oestrin required to produce the various phenomena of oestrus. *J. Physiol.*, **69**, 372 (1930).

(91) Mazer, C., and Goldstein, L.: Clinical Endocrinology of the Female. (Saunders, Philadelphia. 1932.)

(92) Parkes, A. S.: The Internal Secretions of the Ovary. (Longmans, London. 1929.)

(93) Pratt, J. P., and Allen, E.: Clinical tests of the ovarian follicular hormone. *J. Am. Med. Assoc.*, **86**, 1964 (1926).

(94) Ralls, J. O., Jordan, C. N., and Doisy, E. A.: An improved procedure for the extraction of the ovarian hormone and some chemical properties of the product. *J. Biol. Chem.*, **69**, 357 (1926).

(94a) Sandulesco, G., Tchung, W. W., and Girard, A.: Contribution a la connaissance des hormones sexuelles femelles. *Compt. Rend. de l'Acad. des Scienc.*, **196**, 137 (1933).

(94b) Schwenk, E., and Hildebrandt, F.: Ein neues isomeres Follikel-hormon aus Stutenharn. *Naturwissenschaften*, **20**, 658 (1932).

(94c) Smith, E. R., Hughes, D., Marrian, G. F., and Haslewood, G. A. D.: A new triol from the urine of pregnant mares. *Nature*, **132**, 102 (1933).

(95) Smith, G. van S., and Smith, O. W.: The rôle of progestin in the female reproductive cycle. *J. Am. Med. Assoc.*, **97**, 1857 (1931).

(96) Stockard, C. R., and Papanieolaou, G. N.: Existence of a typical oestrus cycle in the guinea-pig, with a study of its histological and physiological changes. *Am. J. Anat.*, **22**, 225 (1917).

(96a) Thayer, S. A., Levin, L., and Doisy, E. A.: Characterization of theelol. *J. Biol. Chem.*, **91**, 655 (1931).

(97) Thayer, S. A., Levin, L., and Doisy, E. A.: Theelin. Some physical and chemical properties. *J. Biol. Chem.*, **91**, 791 (1931).

(98) Thompson, D. L., and Collip, J. B.: The hormones (Luck's *Annual Review of Biochemistry*, **2**, 231 (1933)).

(99) Turner, C. W.: The mammary glands. In Allen's *Sex and Internal Secretions* (Williams & Wilkins, Baltimore. 1932), p. 544.

(100) Turner, C. W., and Frank, A. H.: The relation between the oestrus-producing hormone and a corpus luteum extract on the growth of the mammary gland. *Science*, **73**, 295 (1931).

(101) Veler, C. D., Thayer, S., and Doisy, E. A.: The preparation of crystalline follicular ovarian hormone: theelin. *J. Biol. Chem.*, **87**, 357 (1930).

(102) Walker, B. S., and Janney, J. C.: Estrogenic substances. II. An analysis of plant sources. *Endocrinology*, **14**, 389 (1930).

(103) Wiesner, B. P.: On the separation of the kyogenic hormone from human placenta. *Edinburgh Med. J.*, Feb. (1930), p. 73.

(104) Zondek, B.: Das Ovarialhormon und seine klinische Anwendung. *Klin. Woch.*, Nr. 27 (1926).

(105) Zondek, B.: Hormonale Schwangerschaftsreaction aus dem Harn bei Mensch und Tier. *Klin. Woch.*, **9**, 2285 (1930).

(106) Zondek, B.: Die Hormone des Ovariums und des Hypophysen-vorderlappens. (Springer, Berlin. 1931.)

Chapter VIII

SECRETIN

Pavlov (11) pointed out that substances in the duodenum, particularly acids, cause a flow of pancreatic juice. The cause of the excitation was attributed to reflex action. Bayliss and Starling (2), working at University College, London, injected 0.4 per cent hydrochloric acid into the duodenum or jejenum of the dog, and they noticed that after a latent period of two minutes there was a marked flow of pancreatic juice. The flow was not stopped even after the exclusion of all nerve centers except the pancreas itself. They then showed that the introduction of acid into an enervated loop of jejenum still caused the production of pancreatic juice. Secretion occurred when all nervous connections of the intestine were destroyed. The injection of acid into the blood produced no effect. The mucous membrane of the intestine was scraped off and triturated with sand and hydrochloric acidi. The product was neutralized, filtered and the filtrate injected into a vein; "and we were naturally delighted to find that a copious flow of pancreatic juice was the result" (1).

The explanation offered by Bayliss and Starling was that the acid from the chyme, upon entering the intestine, converted an inactive substance (pro-secretin), present in the mucous membrane, into an active substance (secretin), which found its way into the blood and instigated the pancreas to activity. "Secretion of the pancreas is normally called into play not by nervous channels at all but by a chemical substance which is formed in the mucous membrane of the upper parts of the small intestine under the influence of acid and is carried thence by the blood stream to the gland

cells of the pancreas. . . This secretion is probably produced
by a process of hydrolysis from a precursor present in the
cells which is insoluble in water and alkalis and is not destroyed by boiling alcohol" (2).

Secretin, the name given to the active substance, is not an
enzyme.   Bayliss and Starling showed that it is not destroyed when boiled.   On the other hand, the secretin is destroyed by pancreatic juice and by oxidizing agents.   It is
not precipitated from a watery solution with tannic acid,
alcohol or ether.   It is destroyed by most metallic salts and
is slightly diffusible.   This secretin cannot be prepared from
any part of the body other than the small intestine (2).
Neither is the secretin specific for each type of animal;
"it is common to all types of vertebrate animals" (3).

It was the discovery of secretin which led to a name for
substances like secretin which are manufactured by the
glands of internal secretion.   Hardy proposed the name
hormone, derived from the Greek and meaning "I arouse to
activity" (1).[1]

Source of secretin

Using a method for preparing secretin which has invariably given good results when applied to the duodenal mucosa,
Ivy attempted to extract the hormone from various body
tissues and from spinach, but without success (7).   Neither
was Weaver or Still more successful (14).

PROSECRETIN

Bayliss and Starling were of the opinion that the secretion
of pancreatic juice is probably produced by the acid hydrolysis of a precursor, to which the name *prosecretin* had been
given (see p. 196).   Their view received support from the

[1] It may be said in passing that many papers have appeared since 1902
(when Bayliss and Starling published their work) which tend to disprove
the secretin theory.   However, the weight of the evidence today is very
definitely in favor of it.   See, more particularly, Ivy's papers (7).

fact that active preparations could not be obtained by treating the mucosa with neutral solutions or alcohol, in both
media of which the secretin, once extracted with hydrochloric acid, is soluble.   It has been shown, since the time
of Bayliss and Starling, that several reagents are able to
extract secretin (in moderate quantity, to be sure) from the
duodenal mucosa; such as solutions of sodium chloride,
glycerine and sodium hydroxide (dilute), and alcohol.   But
none of these are as effective as acid (14).   There may or
there may not be a prosecretin; the question is still an open
one.

Preparation

The crude method of preparing secretin which Bayliss and
Starling employed has been given (see p. 196).   The extract,
of course, contained many impurities, and its injection
caused marked vasodilatation.   An early method which
gave promise was one due to Dale (5), who found that secretin forms a mercury compound which is soluble in moderately
dilute acids but insoluble in neutral or weakly acid solutions.
Furthermore, the hardening of the mucous membrane with
corrosive sublimate prevents the extraction of many impurities.

In Dale's method, the superficial layers of mucous membrane are scraped from the upper two-thirds of the small
intestine of a dog or cat, and these scrapings are ground with
one-fifth their weight of mercuric chloride.   Two cubic centimeters of water is added for each gram of mucous membrane.
(The material can be accumulated in this form and apparently
kept indefinitely.)   The contents are boiled and filtered.
The filtrate is rejected.   The coagulum is squeezed dry.
The press cake is suspended in 2 per cent acetic acid with 1
per cent mercuric chloride (about 4 cc. being used for each
gram of original mucous membrane).   The mixture is heated
to boiling and filtered.   To the filtrate a 10 per cent solution

of sodium hydroxide is added until it is nearly neutral; that is to say, until the yellow precipitate of mercuric oxide which forms just fails to be permanent when the solution is shaken. The white precipitate is secretin. The precipitate (A) is suspended in water and hydrogen sulfide passed into it. The acid mixture is neutralized, boiled to get rid of the hydrogen sulfide and filtered from the mercuric sulfide. The filtrate contains the secretin. (An alternative method is to suspend the precipitate (A) in 75 per cent alcohol and to proceed as above.) The filtrate is treated with an excess of acetone, when the secretin precipitates (B). By dissolving this precipitate in water and adding picric acid, an active amorphous picrate can be formed, which, if desired, can be dissolved in dilute sodium carbonate and injected. However, for ordinary purposes, the preparation obtained at stage (B) will serve. The low yields and the fact that the final product is not altogether free from dilator substances, have combined to make this method a rather unpopular one.

A very simple method, and one which reduces the vaso-dilatin contents of the final product to a minimum, was developed by Luckhardt and his co-workers (10). The first 150 cc. of the dog's intestine are excised, and tap water is passed through the loop. One hundred fifty cubic centimeters of 0.2 to 0.4 per cent hydrochloric acid are introduced into the loop and the ends closed with hemostats. At the end of 30 minutes the extract is filtered. The filtrate is ready for use (A). The injection of 5 to 10 cc. of this extract into a dog weighing 10 to 14 kg. and under barbital-sodium anesthesia produces a copious pancreatic secretion. The extract is usually clear or straw-colored, contains no heat coagulable proteins and can be injected intravenously.

Luckhardt and his co-workers, Weaver and Koch (17), were responsible for a still more complete separation of the secretin from the vasodilatin by precipitating the active principle with sodium chloride. The extract (A), prepared as above, is saturated with solid sodium chloride. The precipitate which forms floats on the surface of the solution and can be decanted or filtered. To free the precipitate from any adhering vasodilatin, it is washed several times with 0.4 per cent hydrochloric acid saturated with sodium chloride. The precipitate, containing the secretin, can now be dissolved in a suitable amount of distilled water. It forms a clear to slightly turbid solution and is devoid of vasodilatin effects.[2]

To prepare dogs for injection, rather large animals (from 15 to 25 kg.) are used. These are starved from 1 to 3 days. They are then placed under light barbital anesthesia, barbital sodium (225 to 250 mgm. per kilogram) being injected intravenously or given orally by stomach tube. In 15 to 20 minutes the animal is anesthetized, ether being sometimes necessary during the operative manipulation. The carotid artery is cannulated for a blood pressure record. The saphenous vein is prepared for intravenous injection. The duct of Santorini is next cannulated (the duct of Wirsung is neither cannulated nor ligated). The end of the cannula in the pancreatic duct is brought outside the body and the abdominal wall sutured around it. The dog is now ready for injections.

The crude secretin (A) obtained prior to salt precipitation passes through collodion tubes as well as the vasodilatin. This method was first tried in an attempt to separate vasodilatin from secretin. Another method, which yielded indifferent results, was the attempt to separate the two factors by adsorbing the secretin on permutit and releasing it from the latter with a 10 per cent sodium chloride solution. Dale's mercuric chloride method (p. 198) also had its disadvantages.

Weaver discovered that the secretin present in the sodium chloride precipitate could be dissolved out in 90 per cent

[2] For routine work on the dog this is an excellent method to employ.

alcohol and then precipitated with ether (16); which suggested another method of purification.

Further possibilities in purification were suggested by Still (13) when he recommended the precipitation of the active material with trichloracetic acid (a method first used by Ivy), and the removal of inactive material with brucine and pyridine (a method based on Abel's experiences with insulin; see p. 56). The first part of the process is essentially that of Luckhardt and co-workers (see pp. 199 and 200), but for the sake of convenience we shall give the method in full. The duodenum of the dog is removed and at once washed with cold water (which gets rid of débris, etc.). One end is clamped and the duodenum is filled with a solution which contains 100 cc. of concentrated hydrochloric acid and 50 cc. of sulfuric acid for every 20 liters of water. After 30 minutes the extract is collected and centrifuged. For each 100 cc. of the clear liquid 25 grams of sodium chloride are added, and the mixture is thoroughly stirred for 20 minutes. The precipitate, which is identical with that obtained by Weaver, Luckhardt and Koch (p. 199), contains little or no vasodilatin and is a potent secretagogue. The precipitate is dissolved in 100 cc. of 0.5 per cent sulfuric acid at 50°C., and the insoluble fraction is centrifuged off and discarded. To the filtrate is added trichloracetic acid up to 5 per cent. The precipitate is allowed to settle and then centrifuged. The filtrate is discarded.

The precipitate is washed into a beaker with 3 volumes of absolute alcohol and thoroughly triturated. An equal volume of acetone is now added and the product vigorously stirred. For each 100 cc. of the mixture 500 cc. of ether are added, and the solution is violently stirred until the supernatant liquid separates out. The precipitate is collected and dried *in vacuo* at 40°C. This crude secretin is highly active but still contains choleocystokinin (see p. 208), hypoglycemic substances, etc.

Two hundred fifty milligrams of the precipitate are triturated with 25 cc. of 95 per cent alcohol (containing 1 drop of sulfuric acid for every 250 cc. of alcohol). The product is centrifuged. The supernatant liquid is poured off, and the residue is again extracted with acid alcohol. The filtrates, which contain the secretin, are combined (A). The residue contains choleocystokinin, etc. (See, also, p. 208.)

To (A) is added one-twentieth its volume of 1 per cent brucine in alcohol. The product is allowed to stand in the ice-box for one hour. The precipitate contains no secretin. The filtrate is collected and to it is added one-fortieth its volume of pyridine. Whatever precipitate forms at this point is also discarded. To the filtrate is next added 1 volume of acetone and 5 volumes of ether, which precipitates the active material. The precipitate is centrifuged off, after standing 1 hour in the ice-box, and washed 5 times with the mixture of acetone and ether. It is now dried *in vacuo*, yielding, finally, a highly active substance (B).

(B) may be still further purified by making use of the solubility of secretin in methyl alcohol. (B) is extracted with methyl alcohol (99 per cent) for 1 hour, using a Soxhlet. The secretin in the extract is precipitated with the acetone-ether mixture, the precipitate centrifuged, and washed with ether and dried *in vacuo*.

This product in doses of 0.02 to 0.10 mg. per kilogram will cause the secretion of 6 to 10 cc. of panceatic juice in 20 minutes (using a dog weighing 10 kgm.).

Ivy and his colleagues (8), who published their results in the same year (1930) that Still published his, use a method for preparing secretin which differs but in detail from the methods of Luckhardt and Ivy; and yet these details are of importance; so that here again we shall offer no excuse for giving the method in full. "Dr. Ivy and I have exchanged products," writes Still (14), "and according to our independent assays have found them to be of about equal potency."

In an earlier paper (9), Ivy describes a method which, up to a certain point, serves equally well for the preparation of secretin and for choleocystokinin (see p. 208). The first 6 feet of the intestine are removed, within 20 minutes after death, from a freshly slaughtered dog or hog. The intestine is tied at one end and filled with 100 cc. (if a dog) or 200 cc. (if a hog) of 0.4 per cent hydrochloric acid. The other end is now tied. (The intestine may also be turned inside out, tied at both ends and immersed in 0.4 per cent hydrochloric acid, with occasional stirring.) At the end of 30 minutes the acid solution is removed. The extraction is repeated 3 times. The acid extract is strained through gauze. To the filtrate is added 25 to 30 grams of salt per 100 cc. of solution, yielding the type of precipitate which has already been discussed several times.

Three hundred grams of this precipitate are suspended in 1500 cc. of 95 per cent alcohol (giving a concentration of alcohol of 70 to 85 per cent).[3] Most of the secretin goes into solution. The product is filtered, and the residue is again extracted with 1500 cc. of alcohol. The filtrates are combined. The alcoholic extracts are evaporated to dryness on a water bath. (The residue, the authors state, contains a secretin soluble in water (S-I) and another soluble in 0.4 per cent hydrochloric (S-II),—a somewhat vague statement of the possibility of two kinds of secretin.) The residue is suspended in 2000 cc. of water and allowed to stand for 10 to 12 hours. Sodium hydroxide is now added until the pH is 5.3 to 5.7. When a pH of 5 has been reached, alkali is added very cautiously, because not more than an amount which will cause maximum flocculation is desirable. The exact pH of this "isoelectric point" varies with each batch. The product is filtered. The secretin is present both in the filtrate (S-I, the water-soluble secretin) and in the precipitate (S-II, the

[3] At this point the lower the concentration of alcohol the more choleocystokinin will go into solution.

acid-soluble secretin). Enough 20 per cent trichloracetic
acid is added to (S-I) to make a 5 per cent solution, which
precipitates the secretin. The product is allowed to stand
in the ice-box for 4 to 12 hours, when it is centrifuged and the
precipitate is washed with anhydrous acetone (aldehyde-
free) and ether. (S-II) is suspended in 1500 cc. of 0.4 per
cent hydrochloric acid, filtered, and the filtrate treated with
trichloracetic as under (S-I). The precipitate is washed with
acetone and ether. Both (S-I) and (S-II) are highly active.

The "threshhold dose of secretin" is defined by Ivy as that
amount of dried material in solution which, when injected
intravenously, will cause a ten-drop (0.4 cc.) increase in the
rate of flow of pancreatic juice, within a ten-minute period
following the time of injection, as compared with the preceding ten-minute period.

One of the latest methods for preparing secretin, due to
Cunningham (4), "combines the best features" of several
of the methods of Luckhardt, Ivy, Still, etc. The preliminary operations, involving the preparing of the crude secretin
(extraction with 0.4 per cent hydrochloric and saturating
with salt) we have already given. The next step, the "de-
proteinization," involves heating to coagulate the proteins,
thereby decreasing their adsorptive property over secretin.
For this purpose, the precipitate obtained with sodium
chloride is mixed with enough 0.4 per cent hydrochloric acid
to form a thin cream and then heated to boiling. While
boiling, the mixture is first brought to pH 4.0 with 2 N sodium hydroxide and then to pH 6.0 with 5 per cent sodium
acetate solution. The solution is filtered hot through muslin
and filter paper and allowed to cool. The precipitate of
coagulated protein is rejected.

The filtrate is next treated with trichloracetic acid (p. 201).
Enough trichloracetic acid is added to the filtrate to make
a 5 per cent solution. The precipitate which forms is allowed to stand in the refrigerator for one hour, at the end of

which time it is centrifuged off, washed with aldehyde-free acetone and ether and dried. This precipitate (A) contains all the secretin, together with some protein, but is free from depressor substance and bile pigments. It can be stored for 3 months in the refrigerator without deterioration.

The precipitate (A) is extracted with 85 per cent neutral alcohol (1 cc. for every 10 mgm. of solid product) for one hour at 40° to 50°C. This dissolves the secretin nearly completely and a minimum quantity of protein, etc., accompanies the hormone into solution. The insoluble residues are centrifuged off. The purification with brucine and pyridine, suggested by Still (see p. 201), was not used because of serious losses in secretin activity; but the secretin in the alcoholic filtrate was precipitated by the addition of one volume of aldehyde-free acetone and five volumes of ether. The precipitate is centrifuged off, washed with acetone and ether and dried. This product (B) is free from insoluble protein but contains some sodium chloride.

The precipitation as picrate—the next step— is an adaptation of Dudley's method for the purification of insulin (p. 41). The precipitate (B) is dissolved in distilled water to make a 1.5 per cent solution, centrifuged, if necessary, and the liquid treated with half its volume of saturated picric acid solution and stirred thoroughly. The product is kept in the refrigerator for 24 hours and centrifuged. The precipitate is rubbed up with a dilute solution of acetic acid (5 cc. of saturated solution in 100 cc.) and centrifuged. This washing is repeated twice, thereby getting rid of sodium chloride. The washed picrate is dissolved in a volume of alcoholic hydrochloric acid solution (1 cc. of 3 N hydrochloric acid to 3 cc. of absolute alcohol) equal to the original volume of saturated picric acid used. The insoluble material is centrifuged off and discarded. The solution is diluted with 10 volumes of aldehyde-free acetone. The white precipitate is centrifuged off, washed twice with acetone and ether and

dried over sulfuric acid *in vacuo*. The product, containing
the secretin, is free from depressor substance, insoluble proteins, sodium chloride and picric acid.

Using the "threshhold dose" of Ivy as an assay unit (see
p. 204), this product, a "hydrochloride," is active when 0.5
mg. is used.

Properties

Some of the properties of the products prepared by Ivy,
Still and Cunningham are here given (see (5) and (1B)):

	IVY	STILL	CUNNINGHAM
PO₄	−	−	
S	+	+	+
Biuret	+	?	+
Xanthoproteic	−	−	+
Millon	−	−	+
Pauly	+	?	+
Ninhydrin		−	−
Molisch	−	−	−
Hopkins-Cole	−	−	+
Pettenkofer	+	−	
Ash	0.8		
Hypoglycemic substances		−	
Liver stimulation	+	+	
Choleocystokinin	−	−	

Like the parathyroid hormone, we are here still dealing
with an impure product, and therefore whatever properties
for it we may deduce are but tentative. Some believe the
hormone to be a secondary proteose or polypeptid; others deny
this. The latter group claim that α-amino acids are not
present in the molecule. Tyrosine, histidine, tryptophane
and phenylalanine are not present.

Keeping in mind the impurity of the various products,
it may be said that secretin is apparently soluble in water
and in alcohol up to 90 per cent or so, and partially soluble
even in absolute alcohol and methyl alcohol (+99 per cent).

Precipitates of varying quantity are produced with ammonium sulfate, picric, tannic, phosphotungstic and trichloracetic acids. The secretin is insoluble in ether, acetone, chloroform and benzene. The material can be boiled for one hour with water without destruction. It is best kept in the ice-box around pH 3.0.

Assay

Ivy's assay method, his "threshhold dose," has already been given (p. 204). Still (14) uses a potent, vasodilatin-free prepration which is preserved as a standard and to which all preparations are compared. Four milligrams of this standard administered intravenously into a dog will cause the pancreas to secrete at about 50 per cent of its maximum rate. All injections are made when the rate of pancreatic flow is 1 drop in 4 minutes. The standard (4 mg.) is injected and as soon as the rate returns to 1 drop in 4 minutes, the unknown is injected (in such quantity as to be nearly equal to the standard) and followed by another dose of the standard. The calculation is the number of drops of the unknown + the average number of drops of the standards. This gives the number of units in the amount of unknown injected.

Wilander (18) soaks up the pancreatic secretion during the first 10 minutes in filter paper, which is then boiled with an excess of 0.1 N hydrochloric acid and back titrated with 0.1 N sodium hydroxide. The secretory response is measured in the amount of 0.1 N hydrochloric acid used. Fifteen milligrams of a preparation by Wilander uses 0.6 cc. of the acid. The activity of the unknown is expressed in terms of this standard. The quantity which uses up 0.1 cc. of 0.1 N hydrochloric acid is taken as the unit of secretin, using a cat which has been tested with 15 mg. of the standard preparation.

These standards are no better (and no worse) than the

standard set up for any other hormone which has not been obtained in the chemically pure state; which means that the quantitative character of the test is in need of improvement.

GASTRIN

Edkins as far back as 1906 (6) proposed the theory that a hormone is responsible for the flow of gastric juice; and to this hormone he gave the name *gastrin*. He made extracts of the pyloric mucous membrane with boiling water or 0.4 per cent hydrochloric acid and found that such extracts, when injected into the blood vessels of an animal, lead to a secretion of gastric juice. Around this experiment of Edkins a great deal of dispute has arisen. It may be said at once that no gastrin has so far been obtained in even such concentrated form as has secretin. Transplantation experiments and vivi-dialysis do indicate a humoral mechanism for gastric secretion (7). In a recent contribution, Ivy and his co-workers (12) record the isolation of histamine (as a sulfate) from the pyloric mucosa of the hog "under conditions which preclude the possibility that it is present as a result of putrefactive changes. . . . Our evidence indicates either that histamine is the gastric hormone, or if not, there is no gastric hormone, or the gastric hormone has never been extracted from pyloric mucosa." Histamine (0.5 to 1.0 mgm.), pilocarpine (5 to 10 mg.) and iso-pilocarpine (10 mg. are the only imidazoles out of ten which have been tried that stimulate gastric secretion.

CHOLEOCYSTOKININ

That secretin as usually prepared stimulates the hepatic cells resulting in an augmentation of the flow of bile, is commonly believed (see, for example, (15)). Ivy and his co-workers have succeeded in separating the gall-bladder hormone (which they call *choleocystokinin*) from secretin (9). In their preparation of this substance, the preliminary steps are the same as for secretin (see p. 202), involving extraction of the mucous membrane with hydrochloric acid and precipitation of the hormone with salt. At this point, if choleocystokinin is desired, the precipitate is dissolved in water and the solution brought to a pH of 5.0 to 5.5. The product is filtered. The filtrate is the active portion. This filtrate is treated with trichloracetic acid up to 5 per cent, yielding an active precipitate. The precipitate is washed with acetone and ether. It is soluble in water (1 per cent solution), 95 per cent phenol and 70 per cent alcohol; but more insoluble in alcohol above 70 per cent (which is the basis for its separation from secretin). The assay consists in clamping the cystic duct, cannuling the gall bladder through the fundus or dome and connecting the cannula with a recording tambour. The injections (using dogs) are made into the femoral vein. 1 mg. of Ivy's preparation will cause a vigorous increase in the tone rhythm of the dog's gall bladder (5) (7A).

REFERENCES

(1) BAYLISS, W. M.: Principles of General Physiology. (Longmans, Green and Co., London. 1915.)

(2) BAYLISS, W. M., AND STARLING, E. H.: The mechanism of pancreatic secretion. *J. Physiol.*, **28**, 325 (1902).

(3) BAYLISS, W. M., AND STARLING, E. H.: On the uniformity of the pancreatic mechanism in vertebrata. *J. Physiol.*, **29**, 174 (1902).

(4) CUNNINGHAM, R. N.: Studies on the chemical nature of secretin. *Biochem. J.*, **26**, 1081 (1932).

(5) DALE, H. H., AND LAIDLAW, P. P.: A method of preparing secretin. *J. Physiol.*, **44**, XI (1912).

(6) EDKINS, J. S.: The chemical mechanism of gastric secretion. *J. Physiol.*, **34**, 133 (1906).

(7) IVY, A. C.: The rôle of hormones in digestion. *Physiol. Rev.*, **10**, 282 (1930).

(7a) IVY, A. C.: The physiology of the gall bladder. *Physiol. Rev.*, **14**, 1 (1934).

(8) IVY, A. C., KLOSTER, G., DREWYER, G. E., AND LUETH, H. C.: The preparation of a secretin concentrate. *Am. J. Physiol.*, **95**, 35 (1930).

(9) IVY, A. C., KLOSTER, G., LUETH, H. C., AND DREWER, G. E.: On the preparation of "choleocystokinin." *Am. J. Physiol.*, **91**, 336 (1929).

(10) LUCKHARDT, A. B., BARLOW, O. W., AND WEAVER, M. M.: Note on a rapid and simple method of preparing a highly active pancreatic secretin solution. *Am. J. Physiol.*, **76**, 182 (1926).

(11) PAVLOV, I. P.: The Work of the Digestive Glands. (Griffin, London. 1910.)

(12) SACKS, J., IVY, A. C., BURGESS, J. P., AND VANDOLAH, J. E.: Histamine as the hormone for gastric secretion. *Am. J. Physiol.*, **101**, 331 (1932).

(13) STILL, E. U.: The physiology of secretin. I. Preparation and isolation. *Am. J. Physiol.*, **91**, 405 (1930).

(14) STILL, E. U.: Secretin. *Physiol. Rev.*, **11**, 328 (1931).

(15) STILL, E. U., McBEAN, J. W., AND RIES, F. A.: The physiology of secretin. IV. The effect on the secretion of bile. *Am. J. Physiol.*, **99**, 94 (1931).

(16) WEAVER, M. M.: Studies on the visceral vasomoter responses to intravenous injection of purified pancreatic secretin. *Am. J. Physiol.*, **85**, 410 (1928).

(17) WEAVER, M. M., LUCKHARDT, A. B., AND KOCH, F. C.: Preparation of a potent vasodilatin-free pancreatic secretin. *J. Am. Med. Assoc.*, **87**, 640 (1926).

(18) WILANDER, D., AND AGREN, G.: Standardisierung von Sekretin. *Biochem. Zt.*, **250**, 489 (1932).

Chapter IX

PLANT HORMONES

Whilst, from time to time, reports of plant hormones have appeared in the literature, the recent work of Kögl and his associates at the University of Utrecht has so overshadowed all that has gone before, that we may well confine ourselves to the results of his studies.

Kögl describes the isolation in a chemically pure state of a substance which affects curvature (cell-stretching) in plants (6) (7) (5) (4) (2) (3).[1] The "growth-substance" to be tested (which, for example, is found in the tips of the coleoptile of oats) is placed in contact with cubes of agar-agar, which allow the active material to diffuse into it. If such cubes are placed on the cut area of the coleoptile, curvature results; and the extent of such curvature is proportional to the concentration of active material introduced. The unit strength (AE) is defined as that amount of material which, at a temperature of 22° to 23° and 92 per cent humidity, will give rise, within two hours, to a bending of 10° of the cut coleoptile, when the active material (absorbed in an agar-agar cube) is placed on one side of the cut coleoptile.

Various sources of the plant hormone were investigated: the tips of oats and corn; fungi (particularly *Rhizopus reflexus*); yeast; *bacillus* coli; human feces; and human urine. Kögl found urine (male and female) to be the most convenient source-material, particularly when dealing with quantity production. He discovered that the active material can be extracted from acid media with organic solvents, such as ether (peroxide-free) or butyl alcohol. The hormone can be extracted from organic solvents with dilute sodium bicar-

[1] Good reviews are found in the first two papers.

211

bonate solution; and after acidification with acetic acid, ether will once again extract the active material.   In other words, the hormone (which Kögl calls *auxin*—"growth-promoting"—and which name we shall henceforth give it) shows the properties of an acid.   The key to the isolation of auxin lies in its acidic character.[2]

The following method may be applied if mixed urine is the raw material (7): 150 liters of urine are acidified with hydrochloric acid (1:1) until the reaction is acid to congo red and evaporated *in vacuo* to a thick syrup (A).   The residue is dissolved in 25 to 30 liters of water, acidified with hydrochloric acid and repeatedly extracted with peroxide-free ether.   The ether extracts are combined, dried over sodium sulfate and evaporated.   The ether residue is taken up with 1 to 3 liters of ether and extracted 8 times with saturated sodium bicarbonate solution, using 500 cc. for each occasion. The combined bicarbonate extracts are acidified with hydrochloric acid until the reaction is added to congo red and then extracted with ether 6 to 8 times.   Some 3 to 4 liters of ether are used for this purpose.   The ether extract is dried over sodium sulphate and evaporated.   The residue (B) weighs 45 grams, as compared to the original thick syrup (A), which weighed 5700 grams, and contains practically all the activity.

The next step, treatment with petroleum ether and ligroin, removes more inert material.   The residue (B) is heated with 400 cc. of petroleum ether (B.P. 40° to 60°) for ½ hour on the water-bath.   Upon cooling, the liquid is carefully poured off, and the residue is again extracted with petroleum ether.   This operation is repeated a third time.   This is followed by heating the residue with 400 cc. of ligroin (B.P. 100° to 120°); and this operation is repeated twice.   The

---

[2] Auxin is an example of a *phytohormone*, in contradistinction to the *zoöhormones* of the animal kingdom.   Since, however, the female hormone can be obtained from the plant kingdom and the auxin from human urine, the distinction need not be pressed too closely.

residue, after treatment with petroleum ether and ligroin, weighs 19.7 grams and contains most of the activity (C).

The residue (C) is dissolved in 300 cc. of 60 per cent ethyl alcohol and extracted 10 times with benzene, using 100 cc. each time. The benzene extracts are combined and they, in turn, are extracted first with water (3 times, using 300 cc. each time) and then with 50 per cent methyl alcohol (3 times, using 300 cc. each time). The methyl alcohol extracts are evaporated to dryness, the residue combined with the watery extracts, and the two repeatedly shaken with ether. The ether extracts are evaporated. The residue weighs 5.5 grams and contains most of the activity (D).

The residue (D) is dissolved in 125 to 150 cc. of 96 per cent alcohol and lead acetate (a concentrated solution containing 5 grams of the salt) is added. The resulting precipitate is inactive. Thirty per cent sodium hydroxide solution is added, drop by drop, to the filtrate until the solution is weakly alkaline (E). The precipitate now obtained is filtered, dissolved in dilute acetic acid and extracted with ether (F). The filtrate from (E), which also contains active material, is acidified with acetic acid and extracted with ether (G). The combined ether extracts (F and G) are evaporated. Residue, some 3.17 grams (H).

The residue (H) is dissolved in 30 cc. of alcohol and 300 cc. of water are added. A slight cloudiness develops. Calcium acetate (a concentrated solution containing 6 grams) and N sodium hydroxide, are added, with repeated shaking, until no further precipitate is formed. The precipitate is filtered off and washed with water and a little alcohol. It is practically inert. The filtrate is acidified with acetic acid and thoroughly extracted with ether. The filtrate is evaporated. The residue weighs about 2.25 grams (I).

The auxin in (I) is converted into its lactone by heating (I) with 10 to 15 cc. of a 1.5 per cent methyl alcohol in hydrochloric acid for 1 hour. The alcohol is next removed *in vacuo*, the residue is taken up in ether, and the ether solution (J) extracted twice with 2 per cent sodium bicarbonate solution and twice with water.   At this stage the hormone is no longer soluble in the bicarbonate but remains as part of the neutral fraction.   The ether solution (J) is finally evaporated. The residue weighs 1.2 grams (K).

The residue (K) is slowly distilled, using high vacuum (0.005 to 0.02 mm. mercury).   Portions of from 400 to 800 mgm. are distilled at one time.   The fraction which distills over between 125° to 135°C. contains the main quantity of the hormone; and this fraction, upon standing in the ice-box (preferably surrounded with "solid ice") deposits crystals which can be filtered and further purified.   (Fractions above and below 125° to 135°C. may also be highly active, but they do not as a rule, deposit crystals.)   The crystals may amount to 179 mg. (L).

In one example, the crystals (L) had a melting point of 190° to 192°.   These were recrystallized 6 times from a mixture of ligroin and ethyl alcohol (1:1), the final melting point obtained being 196°.   The activity of this product (true auxin) was 48 million AE units per milligram.   In another example, the crystals (L) showed a melting point of 169° to 171°. These were recrystallized 4 times from 40 per cent acetone. The final melting point of the product was 173°.   The activity of this product (auxin-lactone) was 35.7 million AE units per milligram.   In working with mixed samples of urine, Kögl sometimes obtained crystals having the melting point 173° and sometimes crystals having the melting point 196°.   The average activity of 1 gram of auxin is equivalent to 50,000,000,000 AE; in other words, a bending of 10° of the cut coleoptile is brought about by $\dfrac{1}{50,000,000}$ mg. (or 1/50,000 *gamma*).

Analysis of the product melting at 196° revealed that

only the elements C, H and O are present. The molecular weight (Rast's method) proved to be 338. Microtitration of the product melting at 173° revealed the properties of a lactone; it gave an equivalent weight of 323. The micro-analyses are in good agreement with the formula $C_{18}H_{32}O_5$ for auxin and $C_{18}H_{30}O_4$ for its lactone.

The relation of auxin to its lactone has also been brought out by the conversion of the former (the acid) into the latter with methyl alcoholic hydrochloric acid.

Auxin can be reduced to dihydro-auxin, $C_{18}H_{34}O_5$, showing the presence of a double bond; and with diazomethane it also forms a methyl ester, $C_{19}H_{34}O_5$, which is inactive. It forms a tri-(dinitrobenzoyl)-auxin (a tri-ester), showing the presence of 3 alcoholic groups. The auxin-lactone can also be reduced—to dihydro-auxin-lactone, $C_{18}H_{32}O_4$. Both auxin and its lactone when oxidized yield as the main product an acid $C_{13}H_{24}O_4$ (5).

Auxin is soluble in the cold in methyl alcohol, ethyl alcohol and ethyl acetate; somewhat less soluble in ether; and in water it goes into solution to the extent of 1 per cent. The hormone is insoluble in petroleum ether and in ligroin, and in the pure condition is scarcely soluble in benzene.[3]

Auxin-lactone is soluble in methyl alcohol, ethyl alcohol and ether; and even more soluble in chloroform and in acetone than is auxin itself. On the other hand, the auxin-lactone is less soluble in water than auxin. The lactone is scarcely soluble in petroleum ether, ligroin or benzene.

The female hormone on the market—the commercial product—has an auxin-like effect; this is due not to the theelin, but to an impurity (auxin?) which, like auxin, is soluble in bicarbonate solution. Crystalline (and therefore pure) theelin has no auxin-like effect.

[3] It is soluble in benzene when impure—another instance of how carefully we must define the conditions when discussing the properties of substances.

TOKOKIN, THE FEMALE HORMONE IN PLANTS

We have already discussed (see p. 183) the presence of the follicular-hormone (theelin) in the expressed residue from the kernels of the palm tree, to which Butenandt has given the name *tokokinin*.   Butenandt has isolated this *tokokinin* in the pure state and has shown its identity with his α-*follikel-hormone*.   The preparation of this tokokinin is carried out as follows (1): 50 kg. of the expressed residue from the palm kernel are extracted 3 times with hot methyl alcohol, the combined alcoholic extracts are centrifuged and the methyl alcohol removed by distillation.   The residue (3.1 kg.) is again taken up with methyl alcohol and the insoluble material removed by filtration.   The alcohol in the filtrate is removed, leaving behind the crude raw extracts (A).

Two hundred grams of (A) are heated with 400 cc. of 6 per cent methyl alcoholic potash for $1\frac{1}{2}$ hours under reflux. The product is distilled to one-half its volume, and the residue is diluted with water up to 2 liters.   The solution is acidified with hydrochloric acid and repeatedly extracted with ether.   The ether extracts are filtered, and the filtrate is extracted with 5 per cent sodium hydroxide until the alkali fraction is no longer colored.   The alkaline extracts are washed three times with ether, and the various ether solutions are combined, and the ether evaporated.   The residue (some 40 grams) is distilled at a pressure of 12 mm. of mercury, and a fraction, boiling below 200°, distills over; this is inactive. The residue in the distilling flask is dissolved in 40 cc. of methyl alcohol and the solution heated on the water-bath with 20 cc. of concentrated hydrochloric acid for $1\frac{1}{2}$ hours. The product is diluted with water, repeatedly extracted with ether, and inactive material is again removed from the ether fraction by treatment with 5 per cent sodium hydroxide.   The alkaline extract is washed with ether and the various ether extracts are combined.   The combined ether fraction is now repeatedly extracted with 10 per cent sodium hydroxide. The tokokinin passes into the alkali (phenolic fraction). The alkaline fraction is acidified and the phenolic (active) fraction is extracted with ether. The ether extract is evaporated. The residue is treated with 50 per cent methyl alcohol and petroleum ether as follows:

For every 5 grams of the residue, 30 cc. of the methyl alcohol are added, which dissolves the material. To this solution is added 5 cc. of petroleum ether and 10 cc. of water. This is now extracted with one-half the total volume of petroleum ether, and the latter fraction is removed. Ten cubic centimeters is now added to the alcoholic solution, whereby a turbidity forms. Extraction with petroleum ether is once again carried out. The alcohol-water solution is diluted with 3 to 4 times its volume of water and thoroughly extracted with ether. The ether extracts are combined, filtered and the ether removed by boiling. The residue (which is alcohol-soluble) is distilled *in vacuo*, whereby at 130° to 165° (using 0.001 mm. mercury) a fraction distils over which eventually crystallizes. Some of the hormone also crystallizes in the distilling flask. The product is recrystallized from ethyl acetate and dilute alcohol. The crystalline product so obtained, with a melting point of 254° to 256°, is identical with Butenandt's α-follikelhormon. The optical rotation, which fluctuates from (α) 159° to 170°, is identical with that obtained with the female hormone. Analysis gives the formula $C_{18}H_{22}O_2$. The benzoate has a melting point of 216°, identical with the benzoate obtained with the female hormone. The same is true with the semicarbazid, with a melting point of 259°. Physiologically tested, both tokokinin and the α-follikelhormon show an activity of 5 million ME units per gram.

REFERENCES

(1) BUTENANDT, A., AND JACOBI, H.: Über die Darstellung eines kyrstallisierten pflanzlichen Tokokinins (Thelykinins) und seine Identifizierung mit dem α-Follikelhormon. *Zt. physiol. Chem.*, **218**, 104 (1933).

(2) Kögl, F.: Auxin, ein pflanzlicher Wuchsstoff. *Die Umschau*, Nr. 40, 1932.

(3) Kögl, F.: Die Chemie des Auxins und sein Vorkommen im Pflanzen und Tierreich. *Naturwissenschaften*, **21**, 17 (1933).

(4) Kögl, F.: Chemische und physiologische Untersuchungen über Auxin, einen Wuchstoff der Pflanzen. *Zt. Angew. Chem.*, **46**, 166 (1933).

(5) Kögl, F., Erxleben, H., and Haagen-Smith, A. J.: Uber ein Phytohormon der Zellstreekung. Zur Chemie des krystallisierten Auxins. *Zt. physiol. Chem.*, **216**, 31 (1933).

(6) Kögl, F., and Haagen-Smith, A. J.: Über die Chemie des Wuchstoffs. Proc. Koninklije Akademie van wetenschappen te Amsterdam, **34**, 1 (1931).

(7) Kögl, F., Haagen-Smith, A. J., and Erxleben, H.: Uber ein Phytohormon der Zellstreckung. Reindarstellung des Auxins aus Menschlichem Harn. *Zt. physiol. Chem.*, **214**, 241 (1933).

AUTHOR INDEX

SUBJECT INDEX

Addison's disease, 124, 130, 138–141
Adrenal cortex. See *cortical hormone*
  lactation hormone of, 144
Adrenal glands, functions of, 143–144
Adrenal hormones, 116–151. See *adrenaline* and *cortical hormone*
Adrenaline, 116–123
  clinical applications of, 122
  constitution of, 119–121
  precursor of, 122
  preparation of, 116–119
  properties of, 121–122
Alpha-hypophamine, 106
Amniotin. See *female hormones*
Androkinine. See *male hormone*
Anterior pituitary lobe, 70
  adrenalotropic hormone of, 97
  carbohydrate metabolism hormone of, 93–94
  clinical applications of, 81
  fat-metabolism hormone of, 92–93
  functions of, 70
  growth hormone of, 81
    preparation of, 81–88
    properties of, 83, 85
    test for, 82, 86
  lactogenic hormone of, 94–96
  sex-stimulating hormone of, 71, 73, 75, 77
    in blood, 80
    preparation of, 73–79
    properties of, 74, 78, 79, 80
    source of, 72
  thyreotropic hormone of, 88–92
Ascorbic acid, 143, 144
Auxin, 212, 213, 214
  chemistry of, 215
  isolation of, 212–215

preparation of, 212
properties of, 215

Beta-hypophamine, 106

Choleocystokinin, 201, 202, 203, 208–209
Choline, 145
Corporin, 183–187
Corpus luteum hormone, 183–187
  preparation of, 185
  properties of, 186
  test methods for, 184
Cortical hormone, 124–142
  in urine, 141–142
  preparation of, 125, 126, 127, 128, 130, 131, 132, 133–138
  properties of, 129, 132
  test for, 124, 125, 128, 129, 130, 132, 133, 134, 136, 137
Cortilactin, 145
Cortin, 131, 132

Desiodothyroxine, 8, 10, 11
Diiodotyrosine, 16, 17, 18, 19
Dioxyestrin. See *female hormones*
Emmenin, 76, 187, 188
Ephedrine, 123
Epinephrine, 116. See *adrenaline*
Equol, 182
Estrane, 178
Estriol, 178
Estrogenic substances, in plants, 182
Estrone, 178
Estrus-producing hormone. See *female hormones*
Estrus-producing substances, isomeric, 181

225

Sans Tache

Sans Tache

IN THE "elder days of art" each artist or craftsman enjoyed the privilege of independent creation. He carried through a process of manufacture from beginning to end. The scribe of the days before the printing press was such a craftsman. So was the printer in the days before the machine process. He stood or fell, as a craftsman, by the merit or demerit of his finished product.

Modern machine production has added much to the worker's productivity and to his material welfare; but it has deprived him of the old creative distinctiveness. His work is merged in the work of the team, and lost sight of as something representing him and his personality.

Many hands and minds contribute to the manufacture of a book, in this day of specialization. There are seven distinct major processes in the making of a book: The type must first be set; by the monotype method, there are two processes, the "keyboarding" of the MS and the casting of the type from the perforated paper rolls thus produced. Formulas and other intricate work must be hand-set; then the whole brought together ("composed") in its true order, made into pages and forms. The results must be checked by proof reading at each stage. Then comes the "make-ready" and press-run and finally the binding into volumes.

All of these processes, except that of binding into cloth or leather covers, are carried on under our roof.

The motto of the Waverly Press is *Sans Tache*. Our ideal is to manufacture books *"without blemish"*—worthy books, worthily printed, with worthy typography—books to which we shall be proud to attach our imprint, made by craftsmen who are willing to accept open responsibility for their work, and who are entitled to credit for creditable performance.

The printing craftsman of today is quite as much a craftsman as his predecessor. There is quite as much discrimination between poor work and good. We are of the opinion that the individuality of the worker should not be wholly lost. The members of our staff who have contributed their skill of hand and brain to this volume are:

Keyboards: Agnes Hartman, Viola Collier, Anna Rustic, Minnie Foard.

Casters: Charles Aher, Kenneth Brown, George Smith, Mahlon Robinson, Henry Lee, Charles Fick, Martin Griffin, Ernest Wann, Norwood Eaton, George Bullinger.

Proof Room: Alice Reuter, Mary Reed, Ruth Kelly, Shirley Seidel, Audrey Knight, Angeline Johnson, Betty Hagins, Virginia Williams, Alice Grabau, Dorothy Fick, Louisa Westcott, Helen Defibaugh, Henry King, Evelyn Rogers.

Composing Room: Austin Uhland, Arthur Baker, Harold Hoover, Charles Bittman, William Sanders, Robert Lambert, Robert Daily, Harry Harmeyer, Anthony Wagner, John Crabill, Everett Stallings, Clarence Wilson, Harry Pullara, Ray Kauffman, Charles Smith, Preston Gatton, Henry Shea, Charles Wyatt, Edward Rice, Richard King, Henry Johansen, George Moss.

Press Room: George Pensmith, George Lyons, Henry Eckart, Hugh Morman, Edward Smith, Richard Bender.

Folders: Laurence Krug, Clifton Hedley.

Cutter: William Armiger.